Differences in Activity Concentrations and Doses between Domestic and Commercial Food Production in England and Wales: Implications for Nuclear Emergency Response

S L Prosser, J Brown, J G Smith and A L Jones

This study was funded by the Ministry of Agriculture, Fisheries and Food, Radiological Safety and Nutrition Division, under contract SA075.

National Radiological Protection Board
Chilton
Didcot
Oxon OX11 0RQ

Approval date: January 1999
Publication date: October 1999
£15.00
ISBN 0 85951 438 2

Abstract

In the event of an accidental release of radionuclides into the environment, MAFF has a statutory responsibility to ensure that a wholesome and safe food supply is maintained to the population of England. MAFF also provides scientific advice on contamination of food by radioactivity to the Welsh Assembly and the Scottish Executive. This responsibility will apply whatever the source of radioactive contamination.

Where foods are produced domestically by individuals, ie in private gardens and allotments, MAFF has no statutory powers to prevent their harvest or consumption. MAFF must therefore rely solely upon the provision of appropriate advice to protect those domestic producers potentially at risk. Advice which has been issued to such individuals and households during past nuclear emergency exercises has been based on assessments carried out for commercially produced foods.

Under contract to MAFF, NRPB has undertaken a desk-top study to review the adequacy of the current MAFF emergency procedures for protecting consumers of foods produced domestically. In particular, the study has examined the validity of basing advice for domestic consumers on commercial food production and consumption, rather than by explicitly considering the domestic situation.

As part of the study, reviews have been carried out of the level and types of domestic food production and consumption in the UK. In addition, comparisons have been made between agricultural practices in commercial and domestic situations. The data from these reviews have subsequently been used to compare the doses received by individuals from consuming contaminated foods from commercial and domestic sources.

The study has concluded that, in general, the current MAFF emergency procedures for protecting the domestic consumer are adequate. In the event of an accident occurring some factors may need more consideration, however. These include differences in growing periods and harvesting dates between commercial and domestic crops and the very high consumption rates exhibited by some domestic food producers.

Contents

1		**Introduction**	**1**
2		**Domestic food production in England and Wales**	**1**
	2.1	Scale of domestic food production	1
	2.2	Types of domestic crops grown	2
	2.3	Crop yields for domestically produced foods	3
	2.4	Agricultural practices: differences between commercial and domestic production	3
		2.4.1 Fruit and vegetables	4
		2.4.2 Goats and chickens	5
	2.5	Identification of food categories for detailed study	9
3		**Domestic food consumption in England and Wales**	**9**
4		**Activity concentrations in foods**	**13**
	4.1	Methodology for fruit and vegetables	13
	4.2	Methodology for goats and chickens	14
		4.2.1 Goats	14
		4.2.2 Chickens	15
	4.3	Influence of some domestic horticultural practices	16
5		**Comparison of domestic and commercial food production**	**17**
	5.1	Comparison of activity concentrations	18
	5.2	Comparison of deposition levels with CFILs	19
	5.3	Time-integrated activity concentrations	22
	5.4	Comparison of doses	22
		5.4.1 Average consumption rates	23
		5.4.2 'Critical group' consumption rates	25
6		**Implications for nuclear accident response**	**25**
	6.1	Activity concentrations	27
	6.2	Doses	28
	6.3	Regional practices	28
7		**Conclusions**	**29**
8		**Acknowledgements**	**29**
9		**References**	**29**

Appendices

A	Agricultural Practices for Domestic and Commercial Production of Crops	**31**
B	Distributions of Consumption Rates for Domestic Consumers	**35**

1 Introduction

In the event of an accidental release of radionuclides into the environment, the Ministry of Agriculture, Fisheries and Food (MAFF) has a statutory responsibility to ensure that a wholesome and safe food supply is maintained to the population of England. MAFF also provides scientific advice on contamination of food by radioactivity to the Welsh Assembly and the Scottish Executive. This responsibility will apply whatever the source of radioactive contamination. In addition to this responsibility, MAFF must ensure compliance with regulations issued by the Council of the European Communities[1,2]. These regulations require that no foods contaminated above specified radionuclide concentrations be marketed within the European Union following a nuclear accident.

Where foods are produced domestically by individuals, ie in private gardens and allotments, MAFF has no statutory powers to prevent their harvest or consumption. MAFF must therefore rely solely upon the provision of appropriate advice to protect those domestic producers potentially at risk. Advice which has been issued to such individuals and households during past nuclear emergency exercises has been based on assessments carried out for commercially produced foods. It has been assumed that by basing advice on the commercial situation, consumers of domestically produced foods will be adequately protected. Inherent in this approach are two assumptions:

(a)   that methods used for the production of domestic food do not increase the radionuclide contamination of the foods relative to that in commercially grown produce,

(b)   that, coupled with any differences in activity concentrations, differences in consumption rates between consumers of domestically produced and commercially produced foods do not increase the doses received.

The purpose of this study was to determine the adequacy of the current MAFF emergency procedures for protecting consumers of domestically produced foods. In particular, the study aimed to establish whether advice based on commercial food production would adequately protect the domestic consumer.

2 Domestic food production in England and Wales

In order to determine the potential application of any advice MAFF might issue concerning domestic food in the event of a nuclear emergency, information on the level of domestic food production is required. A review of information relating to domestic food has been undertaken. This review has included an examination of the scale, quantity and types of foods produced and also the rates at which these foods are consumed. In addition, consideration has been given to the types of gardening practices used in domestic production, particularly where these may differ from commercial agricultural practices.

2.1 Scale of domestic food production

The domestic production of food in England and Wales has declined steadily over the last 50 years[3,4]. Nevertheless, it is still a relatively widespread practice. In general, domestic food production takes place on allotments or kitchen gardens and therefore, for the purposes of this study, attention is confined to these areas only. Small holdings or other areas likely to incorporate a commercial element have been excluded.

Domestic production is largely confined to crop cultivation. Whilst some livestock or poultry may be reared in gardens, allotment holders are prevented from keeping such animals. At the request of MAFF, however, some attention has been directed towards chickens and goats, two of the most commonly reared animals in private gardens.

Information relating to the scale of food production on allotments and kitchen gardens across England and Wales is not widely available. In particular, data for kitchen garden usage are scarce. Some data on the scale of allotment usage have been published by Mintel Leisure Association[4] and the National Society of Allotment and Leisure Gardeners[5]. These data are summarised in Table 1. These data show that, for the majority of gardeners, vegetables are the primary crop grown.

TABLE 1 Allotment statistics for England and Wales

Allotment feature	Statistics	Reference
Number in the UK	$3 \ 10^5$	4
Average size in England and Wales	$2.14 \ 10^{-4} \ km^2$	5
Range of sizes in England and Wales	$1.5 \ 10^{-4} - 2.5 \ 10^{-4} \ km^2$	5
Patterns of land use for average plot in England and Wales	Vegetables – 76% of plot Fruit trees/bushes – 10% of plot Rest (compost, flowers, sheds etc) – 14% of plot	5

2.2 Types of domestic crops grown

For the purposes of this study it is important to be able to determine the types of food that will be of greatest importance when considering an accidental release of radionuclides into the environment. Information on the types of crops grown in allotments and gardens have been collected in surveys undertaken previously[4,5]. A summary of these data, which refer to gardeners who actually grow food on their plots, is presented in Table 2. For example, of the gardeners who grow food in kitchen gardens, 22% grow root vegetables. The data collected indicate that, in general, a wider range of crops is produced in individual allotments compared with gardens and also that a larger number of crops per unit area are grown. It should be noted that some of these foods – for example, salad produce in kitchen gardens – could be cultivated in greenhouses. Consequently, these crops might not be contaminated in the early stages following a release of radionuclides to atmosphere. It was not possible, however, to determine from the statistics the percentage of crops grown in greenhouses or under glass.

Further information on the types of crops most commonly grown on allotments was available from the Royal Horticultural Society[6]. These crops are listed in Table 3.

TABLE 2 Crop types grown domestically

	% of gardeners who grow food	
Crop	Allotments	Kitchen gardens
Root vegetables	98	22
Green vegetables	98	20
Salad produce	90	28
Soft fruit	68	19
Exotic produce*	23	18
Fruit trees	Data not available	28

* Examples include asparagus, artichokes and herbs.

TABLE 3 Fruit and vegetables commonly grown on allotments

Beetroot	French dwarf beans	Radishes
Broad beans	Leeks	Runner beans
Brussels sprouts	Lettuce	Spinach
Cabbage	Marrows	Spinach beet
Carrots	Onions	Spring onions
Celery	Parsnips	Sweet corn
Courgettes	Peas	Turnips
Cucumbers	Potatoes	
Blackberries	Gooseberries	Rhubarb

2.3 Crop yields for domestically produced foods

Studies have been carried out which show that the yield of crops produced domestically can be somewhat higher than that from those produced commercially. Estimations of domestic yields based on data in references 5 and 6 are summarised in Table 4, together with the default yields for commercially produced vegetables used in the NRPB foodchain model, FARMLAND[7]. Given the broad categories of vegetables considered, the yields can only be taken as indicative of those seen across a range of species and these values will depend on the different species grown in domestic and commercial situations. However, the influence of different yields between commercially and domestically produced vegetables on the contamination levels in the food at harvest is not likely to be significant for the range of yields considered. In general, it can be assumed that the interception of deposited activity by the plant is proportional to the yield of the crop for the range of yields under consideration, but that the interception per unit mass is independent[7]. Therefore differences in yield have not been considered in the estimation of contamination levels for the foods considered. Where more produce are obtained and subsequently consumed from a unit area of garden or allotment, compared with commercial agricultural land, this difference will be reflected in the relative consumption rates of these produce.

TABLE 4 Commercial and allotment crop yields

Crop	Allotment[5,6] (kg km^{-2})	Commercial[7] (kg km^{-2})
Green vegetables	$3 \ 10^6$	$1 \ 10^6$
Root vegetables/potatoes	$2 \ 10^6$	$4 \ 10^5 - 3 \ 10^6$

2.4 Agricultural practices: differences between commercial and domestic production

It is important to determine differences in agricultural practices that may exist between commercial and domestic production, so that appropriate advice can be issued to all types of producers on the restriction of consumption or harvesting of crops following an accidental release of radioactivity. A review[8-13] has been carried out to identify the differences between domestic and commercial food production in England and Wales. In particular, the following aspects were addressed:

(a)   types of fruit and vegetables grown,
(b)   horticultural practices,
(c)   delays between harvesting and consumption of foods,
(d)   geographical distribution of production.

Detailed findings from the review can be found in Appendix A.

3

2.4.1 Fruit and vegetables

There are no significant differences between the types of fruit and vegetable grown by commercial and domestic growers. Main crop potatoes and onions are less commonly grown by domestic growers because of the space required and the low cost of the commercially produced crop. Domestic growers, particularly those in the south of England, may grow crops such as tomatoes, sweet corn, radish and spinach outdoors. These are not grown outdoors commercially on a large scale in the UK.

The horticultural practices do not, in general, differ significantly between commercially and domestically produced crops, with the sowing and harvesting periods being comparable. Indicative sowing dates and harvesting periods for commercially and domestically grown green vegetables, carrots, potatoes, legume vegetables and soft fruit are shown in Figure 1. The main difference is for carrots where commercial growers aim to harvest continuously throughout the year in contrast to domestic growers, who harvest over a period of a few months and then store the crop for consumption. The harvesting period for domestically grown legumes is longer than that for the commercially grown crop by about six weeks, starting a few weeks earlier and lasting about another month. Commercially produced soft fruit is harvested over a longer period than domestically produced fruit, with the harvesting period lasting for about one month longer due to the growing of 'everbearer' varieties.

The data available are not sufficient to compare the delay between harvesting and consumption of the various vegetable and fruit crops grown under commercial and domestic conditions. However,

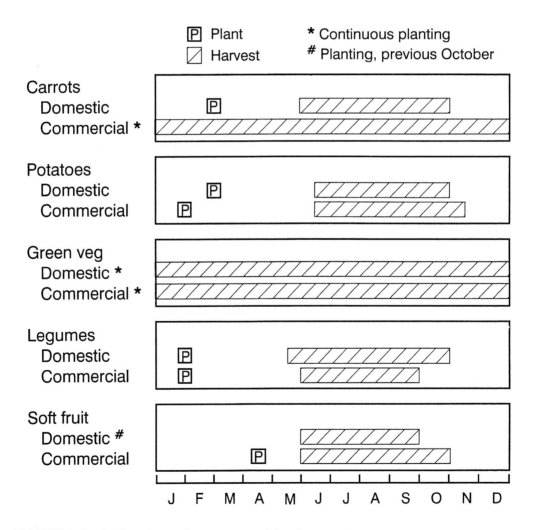

FIGURE 1 Agricultural practices assumed for domestic and commercial production

4

a few observations can be made. Commercially produced vegetables and fruit grown for fresh consumption are largely marketed through retail outlets; this leads to a delay of a few days for products which are not stored. Domestic growers tend to grow and harvest crops on a seasonal basis for immediate consumption and so guarantee a fresh supply of vegetables and fruit over as much of the year as possible. The delay between harvesting and consumption is therefore, in general, likely to be shorter than that from commercially produced vegetables and fruit.

The delays between harvesting and consumption for fruit and vegetables produced commercially for processing and storage are typically up to one to two years. The popularity of 'Pick-Your-Own' farms has also led to some crops, particularly soft fruit and peas, being bought for processing and storage by the domestic consumer. Also, any excess domestic production is likely to be frozen or preserved for consumption outside the harvesting period. The delays between harvesting and consumption for domestically and commercially produced vegetables and fruit that are subsequently processed are likely to be similar, as are those for root vegetables and potatoes which are stored after harvesting.

Most crops grown by domestic growers can be grown throughout England and Wales and the difference between the south and north of England is in the timing of sowing and harvesting, the milder climate in the south enabling both to be possible earlier in the year. Strawberries are, however, less likely to be grown in the north. The commercial production of crops is much less uniform across England and Wales, with specific areas being used for individual crops. Figure 2 shows the principal growing areas for legume vegetables, root vegetables, green vegetables and soft fruit. The primary areas for commercial production of vegetables and soft fruit in England can be summarised as follows:

Green vegetables: fairly uniform across England, excluding the North,
Legumes: West Midlands and South East England,
Potatoes: East England,
Carrots: East Anglia, East Midlands and North West England,
Onions: Central and Southern England,
Soft fruit: Central and Southern England.

The commercial production of fruit and vegetables in Wales is very low and is less than a few per cent of the total production in England and Wales.

2.4.2   Goats and chickens

Goats are kept by a small number of domestic producers for the production of milk and cheese. Domestically reared goats are usually allowed outdoors throughout most of the year. They have a very broad diet and will eat hedgerow plants and broad leaf weeds in preference to grass[13]. Their diet is often supplemented by a wide variety of fodder crops. Commercially reared goats are usually fed stored feed to avoid health problems due to parasites and tainted milk associated with free grazing.

Chickens are kept commercially for the production of meat and eggs, whereas domestic consumers predominantly keep chickens for eggs. Since the aim of this study is to compare differences between the commercial and domestic production of particular foods, attention has been restricted to the consideration of eggs. Laying hens are kept commercially under three different regimes; battery, barn and perch/deep litter, and free range. A study of the diets of laying hens showed that the bulk of the diet is made up of cereals and cereal byproducts, vegetable protein and animal protein[13]. Information on the variation in the dietary composition for free range laying hens and those kept under a deep litter regime is not readily available. Information on the diet of domestically reared chickens is scarce and it is likely that the diet comprises some cereals and some grass[13]. In order to estimate the effect that the different diets may have on the activity concentrations in eggs, it has been assumed that the domestically reared chickens consume only grass.

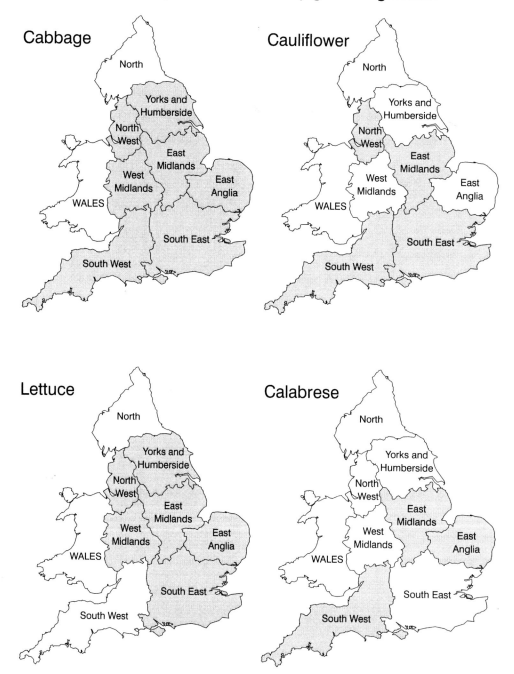

Areas of production for leafy green vegetables

FIGURE 2 Areas of commercial production in England and Wales

6

Areas of production for root vegetables

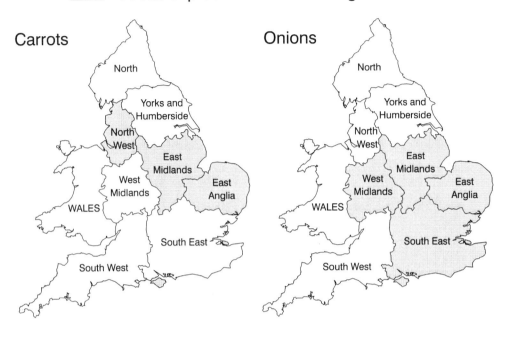

Carrots

Onions

Areas of production for legumes

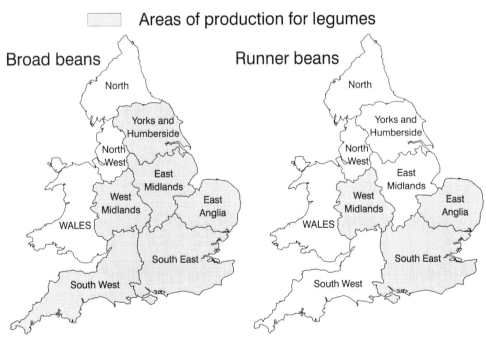

Broad beans

Runner beans

FIGURE 2 *Continued*

Areas of production for soft fruit

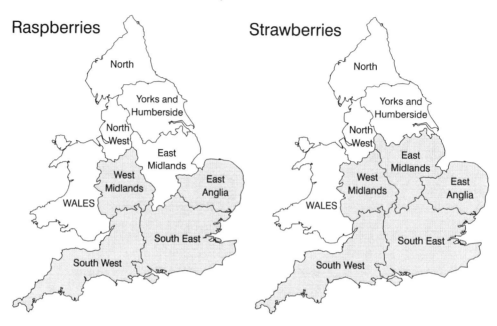

Raspberries

Strawberries

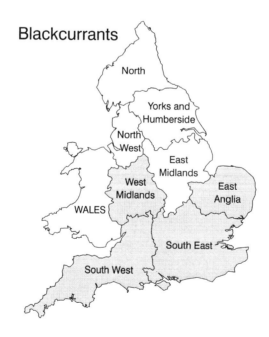

Blackcurrants

FIGURE 2 *Continued*

2.5 Identification of food categories for detailed study

A large variety of fruit and vegetables is grown in allotments and gardens as identified in Section 2.2. These can be grouped together into broad categories of foods for the consideration of the provision of advice on their consumption following a nuclear accident. In defining these groups it is important to take into account any significant differences between horticultural practices for specific fruit or vegetable species and the significance of the consumption of these species by domestic growers. Categories of fruit and vegetables have been chosen for this study based on the reviews of horticultural practices and domestic production and consumption that are described in Sections 2.2, 2.4 and 3, respectively.

The categories that have been chosen are: green vegetables, legume vegetables, potatoes, carrots and soft fruit. Carrots and potatoes have been considered separately both because they form a significant component of root vegetable consumption and because there are potentially important differences in the way they are grown and harvested. For the purposes of this study, an examination of domestically produced animal products has been confined to goats' milk and chickens' eggs. These foods are listed in Table 5.

TABLE 5 Food categories considered in this study

Green vegetables
Legume vegetables
Potatoes
Carrots
Soft fruit
Goats' milk
Chickens' eggs

3 Domestic food consumption in England and Wales

Whilst advice regarding consumption of domestically produced foods may primarily be based on the likely activity concentration levels, it is important also to consider the doses that might be received, and, in particular, how these may differ from the doses that might be received from the corresponding commercially produced foods. In order to make this comparison, data on consumption rates for domestic foods are required. This section discusses the available data and the values used in the dose comparison.

Information on the consumption of domestic food was taken from the MAFF National Food Survey 1993. A summary of the data for 1993 is provided in the annual MAFF National Food Survey report[14]. The data presented in the report enable only the consumption of 'free food' by an average individual in an average household in Great Britain to be estimated. In determining this average, non-consumers of free foods have been included. The free food category utilised for the purposes of the survey is a very generalised one, essentially being defined as foods that enter the household without payment. This category therefore incorporates garden and allotment produce but also includes free gifts from farms etc, where foods are grown using commercial practices. Whilst these averaged and approximate food consumption rates may be suitable for some purposes, information more specific to domestic consumers was required for this study.

For the purposes of this study, therefore, it was necessary to utilise the original survey data and to analyse the information for households where domestically produced food was actually consumed.

The database of survey information was supplied by the Data Archive at the University of Essex on CD-ROM. Information from 1993 was utilised since, at the time of this study, it was the most recent year for which the survey data could be extracted in detailed form. By comparing the data for 1993 with published data from preceding and subsequent years, however, it would appear that the estimated consumption of these foods does not vary greatly from year to year. Consequently, the error introduced by applying the information for 1993 to the current situation in England and Wales was judged to be small in comparison with the errors implicit in the estimations themselves.

The 1993 National Food Survey incorporated information from over 8000 households. Fewer than 100 households consumed domestically grown produce, however. The data provide total consumption by household, together with the number of people in each household (the average number

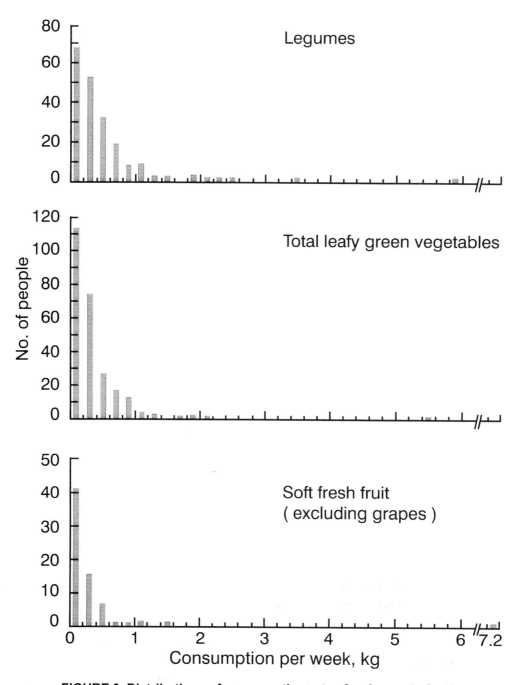

FIGURE 3 Distributions of consumption rates for domestic foods

10

for those households consuming domestic produce was 3.2). 'Household *per caput*' consumption rates were determined by dividing the household consumption by the number of people in the household. It was assumed in this study that these *per caput* values were appropriate for adult consumption rates. In making this assumption, it was recognised that the method employed would underestimate the consumption rates of the highest rate consuming adults, except for those living alone. This under-estimation would be greatest for those in households that included children or infants. However, the data were not appropriate for providing any breakdown of consumption rates by age.

On the basis of these data, distributions of consumption rates have been produced for domestically produced foods. A full set of distributions based on the survey data is presented in Appendix B; those for the five crop categories considered in this study are presented in Figure 3.

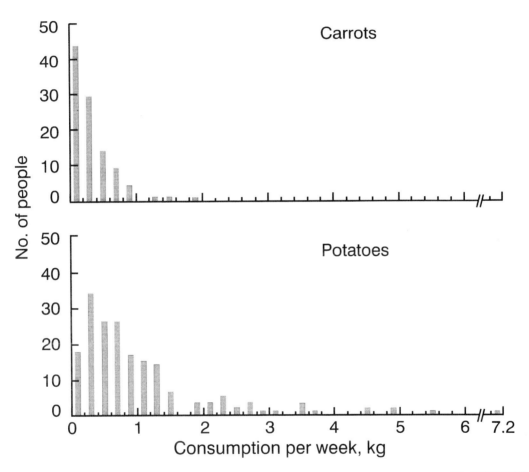

Food	Minimum (g)	Maximum (g)	Total number of people	Mean (g)	Median (g)	95th percentile (g)	97.5th percentile (g)
Green vegetables	17	5,471	252	346	227	963	1,269
Legumes	9	5,897	195	452	43	1,321	1,848
Soft fruit	8	7,257	68	343	151	1,018	1,240
Carrots	13	1,814	103	330	227	902	1,111
Potatoes	14	7,031	195	1,070	726	3,402	4,536

FIGURE 3 *Continued*

It should be noted that these distributions are based on consumption rates which are the sum of foods consumed soon after cropping and those that have been stored and drawn from stock. Since the distributions are highly skewed, median values were selected to represent average adult consumption rates. The 97.5th percentiles were used to provide estimates of adult critical group consumption rates. These consumption rates are presented in Table 6. Similar data for chickens' eggs and goats' milk were scarce. On the basis of very limited data from the survey, a median consumption rate of 52 eggs per year was derived for chickens' eggs. This is rather low, and is certainly lower than the mean consumption rate for the general population. Consequently, the dose comparisons between domestic and commercial egg consumption were carried out assuming generalised consumption rates for both. For goats' milk, consumption rates appropriate for ten year old children were provided by MAFF[15]. However, the degree of uncertainty surrounding this estimate is unclear.

In order to provide appropriate comparisons between the doses to be expected from consumption of domestic and commercial foods, corresponding consumption rates for the general UK population (ie mean and 97.5th percentile of the adult distributions) were adopted as representative of those for commercial foods. These data are presented in Table 7 and are based on information compiled in an NRPB review[16] and data from the National Food Survey[14].

TABLE 6 Household *per caput* consumption rates for consumers of domestic foods

Food type	Median consumption rate (kg y^{-1})	97.5th percentile consumption rate (kg y^{-1})
Legumes	2.2	96.1
Green vegetables	11.8	65.9
Carrots	11.8	57.8
Potatoes	37.8	235.9
Soft fruit	7.9	64.5
Goats' milk*	76 (10 year old children)	137 (10 year old children)

* Value supplied by MAFF; associated uncertainty unknown.

TABLE 7 Generalised adult consumption rates for commercial foods

Food type	Mean consumption rate (kg y^{-1})	97.5th percentile consumption rate (kg y^{-1})
Legumes	1.5	4.1
Green vegetables	15	45
Carrots	7	28
Potatoes	50	120
Soft fruit	1.2	4.5
Cows' milk*	110	240
Eggs	8.5	25

* Consumption rates for 10 year old children, to correspond with the data provided by MAFF for domestic consumption.

4   Activity concentrations in foods

Activity concentrations in commercially and domestically produced fruit and vegetables have been estimated for the radionuclides listed in Table 8. The activity concentrations for all the radionuclides except tritium were obtained by using the NRPB foodchain model, FARMLAND[7]. FARMLAND is a dynamic compartmental model which is flexible enough to take into account the influence of the time of the year of deposition on the resultant activity concentrations in the crops at harvest. The FARMLAND model does not include goats or chickens and a simple approach has been taken to estimate activity concentrations in goats' milk and in eggs, which is described below in Section 4.2. Tritium concentrations have been estimated using TRIF[17], which is a dynamic model for predicting the transfer of tritium through the terrestrial foodchain. TRIF does not consider goats' milk or eggs; however, indicative values for tritium concentrations in goats' milk are discussed.

TABLE 8 Radionuclides considered in the study

Tritium	Ruthenium-103,106	Cerium-144
Sulphur-35	Tellurium-132	Promethium-147
Cobalt-60	Iodine-129,131,133,135	Plutonium-239,240,241,242
Rubidium-88	Caesium-134,137	Americium-241
Strontium-89, 90	Barium-140	Curium-242,244

4.1   Methodology for fruit and vegetables

For all the radionuclides listed in Table 8, except tritium as mentioned above, FARMLAND was used to determine radionuclide activity concentrations at harvest for foods grown under both domestic and commercial regimes. In each case, the maximum concentration found in the food over the first harvesting period following deposition was determined, together with the time-integrated activity concentrations in the crop for the first and second years following deposition. In order to investigate the influence of time of deposition on the activity concentration at harvest, these concentrations were predicted for deposition occurring 1 day, 30 days, 60 days, 90 days and 120 days before the start of harvest. Where harvesting occurs over a period, the time of deposition has been taken as the number of days before the start of harvesting.

The agricultural practices that have been assumed are based on the review of current practices in England and Wales, as described in Section 2. Some of the agricultural practices are quite complex, with different varieties or species of a generic crop category being grown over a season. In this study, broad categories of crops are being considered, as described in Section 2.5 and so the practices have been combined and simplified for use in the model. Tables 9 and 10 summarise the assumptions used in FARMLAND for domestically and commercially grown fruit and vegetables.

For tritium, a simpler approach has been taken using the results of the TRIF model[17]. TRIF considers only a single broad category of vegetables and the assumption is made that the vegetables are continuously harvested throughout the year. The activity concentrations for green vegetables can be taken as indicative upper bounds for the other vegetable and fruit categories considered in this study. TRIF has been used to determine the maximum activity concentration in vegetables following deposition occurring 1 km downwind from the release. This maximum activity concentration typically occurs about five days after deposition. For the calculations it has been assumed that all the tritium released and deposited is in the form of tritiated water[*]. In using the TRIF model results, the implicit

---

[*] This is a more conservative assumption than allowing for a component of tritium gas.

TABLE 9 FARMLAND assumptions for domestically produced crops

Crop	Planted/sown	Harvest period	Fallow period	Comments
Carrots	15 March	1 June – 30 Sept	16 Oct – 14 March	Harvested for immediate consumption
		1 Oct – 15 Oct		Harvested for both immediate consumption and storage
Potatoes	15 March	11 June – 15 Oct	16 Oct – 15 March	–
Soft fruit	1 Oct	26 May – 30 Sept	–	–
Leafy green vegetables	Throughout year	Throughout year	–	Includes: brassicas, salad vegetables and other leafy green vegetables which, considering all species together, are grown fairly continuously over the year
Legume vegetables	1 Feb	15 May – 31 Oct	1 Nov – 31 Jan	Peas and beans

TABLE 10 FARMLAND assumptions for commercially produced crops

Crop	Planted/sown	Harvest period	Fallow period	Comments
Carrots	Throughout year	Throughout year	–	–
Potatoes	1 Feb	16 June – 31 July	16 Nov – 31 Jan	'Early' crop for immediate consumption
		1 Aug – 15 Nov		'Main' crop for both immediate consumption and storage
Soft fruit	16 April	26 May – 31 Oct	1 Nov – 15 April	Assumptions for strawberries, the dominant contributor to consumption and production
Leafy green vegetables	Throughout year	Throughout year	–	Includes: brassicas, salad vegetables and other leafy green vegetables which, considering all species together, are grown fairly continuously over the year
Legume vegetables	1 Feb	1 June – 30 Sept	1 Oct – 31 Jan	Peas and beans

assumption is made that the crop is growing at the time of deposition. Information on the activity concentrations as a function of time following deposition has been used to give an indication of possible differences that might be seen when different horticultural practices are used for domestic and commercial crops. The total time-integrated activity concentrations in vegetables and fruit have also been estimated from the results of the TRIF model. It is reasonable to assume that by the end of the first year the activity concentrations in vegetables and fruit are negligible[17] and that the total integrated concentration is appropriate for the first year after deposition. The time-integrated activity concentrations in the second year after deposition can therefore be assumed to be zero.

4.2 Methodology for goats and chickens

4.2.1 Goats

In order to estimate activity concentrations in goats' milk, information on the transfer of sulphur, strontium, caesium, iodine and plutonium to goats' milk, on daily milk yields and on consumption rates has been obtained from the literature. Goats typically eat about 2.5 kg d^{-1} dry matter and produce, on average, about 3 l d^{-1} of milk[18]. The transfer of radionuclides to goats' milk is reported to a limited extent in the literature[18–21]. The experimental data suggest that the transfer at equilibrium, expressed in terms of the fraction of the daily intake transferred to a litre of milk, is of the order of a factor of ten higher than the transfer to cows' milk, for most elements. For iodine, there is some evidence that the transfer may be up to a factor of fifty times higher, but it should be borne in mind that the experimental data were for field trials where very soluble forms of iodine were given. Lengemann[22] showed that iodine transferred from the blood plasma into goats' milk was concentrated by about a factor of five compared to that in cattle. The data in Table 11 summarise the information used.

Although a goat's diet can be very varied, it is reasonable to assume that the contamination of the diet will typically be no higher than that for animals consuming pasture grass. Although some weeds could possibly intercept more activity than grass, other foraged foods are likely to be less contaminated, eg lower parts of hedgerows. If account is taken of the lower daily intake rate of goats and the higher transfer to milk for goats, it can be concluded that concentrations in goats' milk are likely to be around a factor of two to three higher than in cows' milk. For iodine, the activity concentrations could be up to a factor of five to ten higher, although the majority of the data suggest that factors greater than five are unlikely. The limited environmental monitoring of goats' milk carried out in England and Wales by MAFF after the Chernobyl accident[23] supports the observation that activity concentrations in goats' milk are unlikely to be more than a factor of a few higher than those in cows' milk.

For this study, it has been assumed that the concentrations in milk from goats kept by domestic producers will be typically about a factor of three higher than the concentrations in commercially produced milk from cows grazing permanently outdoors for sulphur, strontium, caesium and plutonium. For iodine, a factor of five has been used to allow for the relatively higher transfer suggested by the literature. The activity concentrations in cows' milk have been estimated using the FARMLAND model[7], assuming that the cows are outdoors grazing pasture at the time of deposition, but (for the time-integrated activity concentrations) allowing for a period during the year when they are consuming stored feed.

The contamination of goats' milk by tritium has been considered in a qualitative way. As the fractions of water and fat in cows' and goats' milk are similar[17], it is not expected that the activity concentrations will differ significantly if the diets of the animals are similar. However, in line with the findings for the transfer of radionuclides to goats' milk, it is prudent to say that the activity concentrations could be up to a factor of three higher than those in cows' milk.

TABLE 11 Data used for predictions of activity concentrations in goats' milk and eggs

Parameter	Goats' milk		Cows' milk[7]		Chickens' eggs	
Intake rate (kg d^{-1})	2.5 (grass)		13 (grass)		0.1 (grass or cereals)	
Transfer factor for milk, F_m (d l^{-1}), and for eggs, F_f (d kg^{-1})	S	0.008–0.02	S	0.02	–	–
	Sr	0.006–0.02	Sr	0.002	Sr	0.3
	Cs	0.006–0.1	Cs	0.005	Cs	0.5
	I	0.06–0.7	I	0.005	I	3
	Pu	0.001 (estimate)	Pu	0.0001	Pu	0.008

4.2.2 Chickens

A simple equilibrium transfer approach has been used to estimate activity concentrations of strontium, caesium, iodine and plutonium in eggs from laying hens consuming either only cereals or only grass. This methodology is adequate for the calculation of annual time-integrated activity concentrations and, hence, doses, as equilibrium will have been reached. However, it is inappropriate for estimating the time dependence of radionuclide transfer to eggs. The consumption rates of laying hens and the transfer factors for eggs have been taken from the literature[13,14,24]. Owing to the lack of data for sulphur transfer to eggs, it has not been possible to estimate activity concentrations of sulphur-35 in eggs. However, it is expected that any differences seen between activity concentrations in eggs from laying hens reared under commercial and domestic conditions will be similar to those seen for caesium-137 as both radionuclides are mobile and will behave similarly in the respective feeds. The data used in this study are given in Table 11.

For the cereal diet, deposition occurring at both 30 days and 120 days before the harvest of the cereal crop has been considered. An indication of the maximum concentrations in eggs has been obtained by taking the maximum concentrations in the chicken feed in the first year following deposition and calculating the concentrations in eggs using the equilibrium transfer factors. As noted above, these maximum activity concentrations should only be used to demonstrate the differences between the activity concentrations in eggs produced under commercial and domestic practices and should not be used as realistic maximum activity concentrations in eggs.

4.3   Influence of some domestic horticultural practices

The main differences in horticultural practices for domestically and commercially produced fruit and vegetables are the sowing and harvesting dates; these have been taken into account in the calculation of the activity concentrations predicted using the FARMLAND model. Several other factors, which may influence activity concentrations in fruit and vegetables produced in allotments and gardens and which are not included in the FARMLAND model, have also been considered in a semi-quantitative way. These are:

(a)   the effect of sowing different varieties of a vegetable or fruit species,
(b)   the use of fertilisers,
(c)   irrigation,
(d)   the use of compost.

An experimental programme of measuring the transfer of radionuclides from contaminated soil to a range of varieties of a number of species of vegetables and other crops concluded that variations in the transfer from soil to plant between the different crop varieties were comparable with the differences that were observed for the same variety grown in different years[25]. Therefore, any differences between the varieties grown under domestic and commercial conditions are unlikely to be significant. It should be noted that the experimental programme only considered root uptake and not direct deposition to the crop. The latter will dominate the activity concentrations in the first harvest if deposition occurs within a few months of the harvest. No information has been found on any differences between translocation and weathering for different crop varieties. However, these are likely to be small compared to the importance of the time between the accident and the harvest in governing the maximum concentrations in the first harvest.

The strength of fertilisers used by domestic and commercial producers will be different. However, the basic components in the fertilisers are the same and it is very unlikely that there will be any significant differences in the effect the fertilisers have on the uptake of radionuclides from the soil into the crops via the roots[26].

The implications of the use of contaminated water that has been collected in water butts for subsequent watering of fruit and vegetables grown in gardens has been considered. This is a pathway only likely to be relevant for domestic producers, since commercial growers would require a larger scale and more dependable supply, eg a river or the mains supply which is unlikely to be contaminated to any significant extent after an accident. If deposition occurs during rainfall then contaminated water collected from the roofs of sheds and greenhouses could be collected in a water butt, the worst case being that there is no dilution within the water butt from previous or subsequent uncontaminated rain water. The impact on activity concentrations in crops depends on the relative timings of the initial deposit, the time of watering and the harvesting date. In terms of absolute activity concentrations, the most pessimistic scenario is the irrigation of crops by undiluted contaminated rainwater shortly after the initial deposition, assuming this occurred shortly before the start of harvest, and that the interception by the crop via watering is the same as that during the initial deposition. Assuming equal volumes of rain water were involved in both the initial deposition and the irrigation, then this could have the effect of doubling the maximum activity concentration in the crop. In reality, this theoretical maximum would be reduced, owing to one or more of a number of factors. Such factors include lower interception by the crop during irrigation compared to the initial deposition (eg watering around the base of plants or at high application rates) and the dilution of activity in the water butt from radioactive decay and/or from uncontaminated rain water collected before or after the accident. If there is a significant delay between the initial deposition and the time of irrigation, then this would have an effect similar to the occurrence of a second accident that resulted in wet deposition. Whether this second deposition contributed more or less to the total activity concentration in the crops at harvest would depend on the relative timings of the two events and the uptake of the radionuclides to the edible part of the crop. The potential remains, however, for domestic producers to enhance the activity concentrations in their crops relative to those in commercial crops through the use of contaminated rainwater for irrigation.

Compost made from vegetable waste and grass cuttings is often used in gardens and allotments to improve the soil quality. Typically, about 25–30% of the initial deposition of radionuclides is intercepted by the vegetable plant or grass[7]. This initial activity weathers off the plant surface with time on to the soil, hence increasing the activity in the soil relative to that in the plant, although for grass some of the activity is removed by mowing. For short-lived radionuclides, the activity concentrations in any compost made from the vegetative matter in the garden will be negligible by the time the compost is used. For long-lived radionuclides such as caesium-137 and strontium-90, the addition of the contaminated compost in subsequent years could therefore lead to a maximum increase of activity concentrations in the soil of about 25–30% if the vegetative waste is produced shortly after the initial deposition before weathering occurs. This assumes that the concentrations in the compost remain the same as those in the vegetative matter and that leaching of the activity from the decaying matter, which would reduce the concentrations, does not occur.

5   Comparison of domestic and commercial food production

The activity concentrations in vegetables, soft fruit, goats' milk and eggs calculated as part of this study have been used to provide information on whether advice based on commercial food production is appropriate for domestically produced food in gardens and allotments. Estimates have been made of the deposition levels that would give rise to the activity concentrations specified by the Council of the European Communities (CFILs)[1,2] being exceeded in each food. These estimates have been made for each of the radionuclides listed in Table 8 and for deposition occurring at five different times before the start of harvest. In addition, the committed effective doses arising from consumption of food in the first and second year following deposition have been calculated. In both cases a comparison has been made between the results for domestic and commercial food production.

A full set of the calculations carried out is presented in an accompanying memorandum to this report[27]. A representative sample of the results is discussed here, namely results for tritium, sulphur-35, strontium-90, iodine-131, caesium-137 and plutonium-239 and for deposition occurring 30 days and 120 days before the start of harvest. These results are representative of the full dataset in terms of the conclusions that are drawn.

17

5.1   Comparison of activity concentrations

The differences between the production of domestic and commercial foods may result in differences in the maximum activity concentrations of foods at harvest. This study has shown that, for deposition occurring fairly close to harvest (within about one month) these differences would be small. This reflects the fact that in both cases the crop is in the ground at the time of deposition and the fact that differences between harvesting practices are not important. Figure 4 illustrates this point for three radionuclides (strontium-90, caesium-137 and plutonium-239) and three food categories.

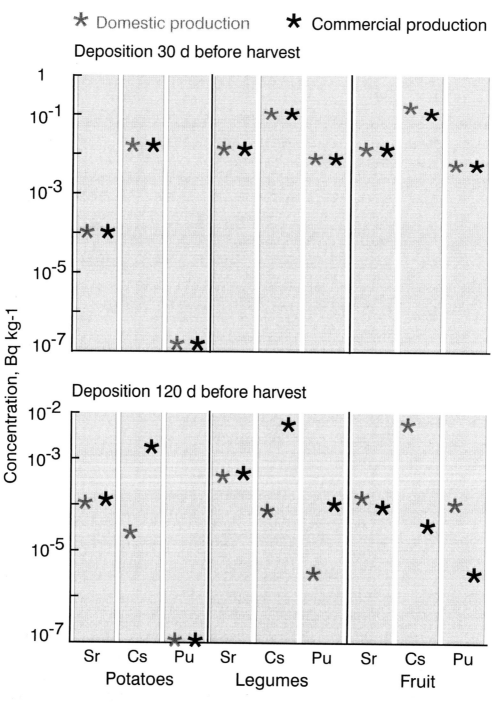

FIGURE 4 Comparison of peak activity concentrations in domestic and commercial foods

For deposition occurring 120 days before the start of harvest some more marked differences are seen. These are also shown in Figure 4. The differences are up to about two orders of magnitude and are not consistent across radionuclides for a particular food. For potatoes and legumes, the domestically grown crop has not been planted 120 days before the start of harvest and so the maximum concentrations are lower than those observed in the commercial crop. For potatoes, the difference is only significant for caesium, reflecting the relative importance of direct deposition and subsequent translocation to the tuber in determining the activity concentration at harvest for this radionuclide. For legumes a difference is seen for both caesium-137 and plutonium-239; this reflects the importance of direct deposition on to the legume vegetables produced commercially. (For plutonium direct deposition does not influence the contamination of the tuber and so no differences are seen for potatoes.) For soft fruit the activity concentrations in the commercial crop are lower than those in the domestic crop, reflecting the fact that the commercial crop is not planted until after the deposition occurs. Again the relative difference between the crops for the different radionuclides reflects the relative importance of the processes governing the contamination of the crop at harvest. In this context, it is important to remember that, although the relative difference might be expected to be large, the actual activity concentrations in crops resulting from deposition that occurs some three months before the start of harvest would be low: an extremely large accident would be required to trigger bans based on the CFILs, if it occurred such a long time before the start of harvest.

5.2 Comparison of deposition levels with CFILs

For convenience, the CFILs specified by the Council of the European Communities[1,2] are reproduced in Table 12. Whilst these levels do not strictly apply to foods that are domestically consumed (ie they are not marketed), in emergency exercises MAFF has used these limits as a basis on which to provide advice to the domestic consumer. Consequently, the CFILs are used in this study as the criteria which MAFF would adopt to trigger advice to avoid consumption of domestic foods.

The maximum activity concentrations per unit deposition predicted by FARMLAND for each food category have been used to determine the deposition level in becquerels per square metre that would give rise to the CFILs being exceeded. The differences in deposition levels directly reflect the differences in the activity concentrations in the crop at harvest. The results for deposition that occurs 30 days and 120 days prior to harvest for commercially and domestically produced foods are presented in Table 13. Where the values differ by more than a factor of two, the lower (ie more restrictive) value is underlined. Since tritium is excluded from the CFILs, results for this radionuclide have not been included in the table.

TABLE 12 Council Food Intervention Levels (CFILs)

	Intervention levels (Bq kg^{-1})				
Radionuclide	Baby foods	Dairy produce (milk and cream only)	Minor foods (eg herbs and spices)	Other foods[*]	Liquid foods
Isotopes of strontium, notably ^{90}Sr	75	125	7,500	750	125
Isotopes of iodine, notably ^{131}I	150	500	20,000	2,000	500
Alpha-emitting isotopes of plutonium and transplutonium elements	1	20	800	80	20
All other radionuclides of half-life greater than 10 days, notably ^{134}Cs and ^{137}Cs (excluding ^{14}C, ^{3}H and ^{40}K)	400	1,000	12,500	1,250	1,000

* All major food items other than milk, and including cheese, meat, vegetables.

TABLE 13 Deposition levels leading to CFILs being exceeded (Bq m^{-2})

Radionuclide	Crop	30 days		120 days	
		Domestic	Commercial	Domestic	Commercial
Sulphur-35	Carrots	$6.7\ 10^4$	$6.9\ 10^4$	$2.4\ 10^6$	$6.9\ 10^4$
	Legumes	$1.4\ 10^4$	$1.4\ 10^4$	$2.4\ 10^6$	$4.7\ 10^5$
	Soft fruit	$1.4\ 10^4$	$1.4\ 10^4$	$4.7\ 10^5$	$2.4\ 10^6$
	Potatoes	$6.7\ 10^4$	$6.7\ 10^4$	$2.4\ 10^6$	$9.3\ 10^5$
	Green vegetables*	$4.2\ 10^3$	$4.2\ 10^3$	n/a	n/a
	Milk‡	$5.8\ 10^2$	$1.7\ 10^3$	n/a	n/a
Strontium-90	Carrots	$3.1\ 10^6$	$5.3\ 10^6$	$3.4\ 10^6$	$5.3\ 10^6$
	Legumes	$5.2\ 10^4$	$5.2\ 10^4$	$1.7\ 10^6$	$1.3\ 10^6$
	Soft fruit	$5.4\ 10^4$	$5.4\ 10^4$	$3.4\ 10^6$	$8.0\ 10^6$
	Potatoes	$5.9\ 10^6$	$6.2\ 10^6$	$6.8\ 10^6$	$5.2\ 10^6$
	Green vegetables*	$2.5\ 10^3$	$2.5\ 10^3$	n/a	n/a
	Chickens' eggs†	$5.0\ 10^4$	$1.3\ 10^6$	$5.0\ 10^4$	$4.6\ 10^7$
	Milk‡	$3.4\ 10^3$	$1.0\ 10^4$	n/a	n/a
Iodine-131	Carrots	$1.2\ 10^6$	$5.2\ 10^5$	$1.2\ 10^{12}$	$5.2\ 10^5$
	Legumes	$2.4\ 10^5$	$2.4\ 10^5$	$7.1\ 10^{11}$	$5.3\ 10^9$
	Soft fruit	$2.4\ 10^5$	$2.4\ 10^5$	$5.3\ 10^9$	$9.2\ 10^{11}$
	Potatoes	$1.2\ 10^6$	$1.2\ 10^6$	$1.2\ 10^{12}$	$4.6\ 10^7$
	Green vegetables*	$6.7\ 10^3$	$6.7\ 10^3$	n/a	n/a
	Chickens' eggs†	$1.3\ 10^4$	$8.9\ 10^5$	$1.3\ 10^4$	$4.8\ 10^{10}$
	Milk‡	$1.4\ 10^3$	$7.0\ 10^3$	n/a	n/a
Caesium-137	Carrots	$5.5\ 10^4$	$5.7\ 10^4$	$6.4\ 10^7$	$5.7\ 10^4$
	Legumes	$1.1\ 10^4$	$1.1\ 10^4$	$1.9\ 10^7$	$2.3\ 10^5$
	Soft fruit	$1.1\ 10^4$	$1.1\ 10^4$	$2.3\ 10^5$	$3.4\ 10^7$
	Potatoes	$5.5\ 10^4$	$5.5\ 10^4$	$5.1\ 10^7$	$5.8\ 10^5$
	Green vegetables*	$4.2\ 10^3$	$4.2\ 10^3$	n/a	n/a
	Chickens' eggs†	$5.0\ 10^4$	$2.3\ 10^5$	$5.0\ 10^4$	$4.3\ 10^6$
	Milk‡	$4.6\ 10^3$	$1.4\ 10^4$	n/a	n/a
Plutonium-239	Carrots	$7.2\ 10^8$	$7.2\ 10^8$	$7.2\ 10^8$	$7.2\ 10^8$
	Legumes	$1.1\ 10^4$	$1.1\ 10^4$	$1.8\ 10^7$	$8.2\ 10^5$
	Soft fruit	$1.1\ 10^4$	$1.1\ 10^4$	$8.2\ 10^5$	$2.1\ 10^7$
	Potatoes	$7.2\ 10^8$	$7.3\ 10^8$	$7.2\ 10^8$	$7.2\ 10^8$
	Green vegetables*	$2.7\ 10^2$	$2.7\ 10^2$	n/a	n/a
	Chickens' eggs†	$2.0\ 10^5$	$1.5\ 10^7$	$2.0\ 10^5$	$5.3\ 10^8$
	Milk‡	$6.4\ 10^6$	$1.9\ 10^7$	n/a	n/a

* 'Harvest' for green vegetables is assumed to be continuous throughout the year and so results are appropriate for all times.

† For commercial chickens fed on cereals, these values refer to deposition occurring prior to the cereal harvest. 'Harvest' is continuous for grass and so the results for chickens on an all grass diet are appropriate for all times.

‡ These values apply to goats' milk for domestic production and cows' milk for commercial production. In both cases, the animals are assumed to be grazing pasture at the time of deposition and the results are appropriate for all times where the animals are grazing outdoors.

MAFF currently bases its advice to domestic consumers on commercially produced foods. Domestic foods are, therefore, only likely to be of concern when the deposition levels giving rise to the CFILs being exceeded are significantly more restrictive for domestic production compared to commercial production. With regard to the crops considered it can be seen, from Table 13, that this situation only occurs for soft fruit (all radionuclides), and then only when deposition occurs a long time before the start of harvest, the example shown being 120 days. The difference between commercially and domestically produced soft fruit arises as a result of differences in the planting times assumed for the domestic and commercial crops. Domestically grown soft fruit bushes are planted in October and the start of the fruit harvest is the end of the following May. For commercially grown soft fruit, however, growing and harvesting periods have been based on strawberries, which are the dominant contributor to consumption and production of these produce. Strawberries have a much shorter growing season, the assumption being made that they are planted in mid-April with the fruit being harvested from the end of May. The lower deposition level required to exceed the CFILs for domestically produced soft fruit reflects the fact that at any time greater than about 45 days before the start of harvest, domestically grown soft fruit will be growing whereas commercially grown strawberries will not. The relative difference in the deposition levels between radionuclides reflects the processes governing the contamination at harvest, as discussed above. It should be noted that although the assumptions made in this study concerning soft fruit (growing periods, harvesting times and types) are believed to be generally representative of the practices in England and Wales, in any specific situation under consideration these assumptions may be inappropriate. However, these results illustrate the extreme case; other plausible assumptions would tend to reduce the expected differences between the activity concentrations in domestic and commercial foods.

For chickens' eggs, the deposition levels are significantly more restrictive for domestically reared chickens compared to those reared commercially for all the radionuclides considered. This reflects the different assumptions made regarding the diet of chickens in the two cases. For domestically reared chickens, the conservative assumption has been made, in the absence of information, that domestic chickens are fed entirely on grass, compared with commercially reared chickens that are fed entirely on cereal based feeds. The maximum activity concentrations in grass will always be higher than those in cereals following deposition on to the crop, particularly for radionuclides which are not readily translocated from the cereal plant to the grain seed. In reality, domestic chickens are likely to be fed on a mixed diet of grass and cereals, which would lower the difference seen. However, eggs from domestically reared chickens will always be more restrictive. It should also be noted that, in reality, the maximum concentrations in commercially and domestically produced eggs will be reached on different timescales after deposition. For chickens consuming grass, the maximum concentrations will be reached shortly after deposition, whereas eggs from commercially reared chickens will contain maximum activity concentrations at the time when contaminated cereals are first fed following the cereal harvest, assuming no measures are put in place to restrict the feeding of contaminated cereals. It should be noted, therefore, that it is likely that only eggs from domestically reared chickens will be contaminated in the short term after deposition.

In this study, it has been assumed that the activity concentrations in goats' milk are three times higher than those in cows' milk for sulphur-35, strontium-90, caesium-137 and plutonium-239 and a factor of five higher for iodine-131, for the same level of deposition on grass (see Section 4.2). The deposition levels given in Table 13 were determined by using FARMLAND[7] to estimate those applicable to cows' milk, assuming the cows were grazing outdoors at the time of deposition. These were then scaled to obtain the appropriate values for goats' milk. The uncertainties surrounding this assumed ratio should be recognised, although measurements made after Chernobyl indicate that it is unlikely to be a gross underestimate.

5.3 Time-integrated activity concentrations

In general, time-integrated activity concentrations in crops, for the first year following deposition, reflect the differences seen in the maximum activity concentrations discussed above. The exception is carrots, where differences in harvesting methods between the domestic and commercial situation give rise to relatively higher time-integrated activity concentrations in domestically produced carrots, although the maximum activity concentrations are very similar.

For milk and eggs, however, differences in husbandry practices between commercially and domestically reared animals give rise to differences between the time-integrated activity concentrations which are not necessarily the same as those observed in the maximum activity concentrations. The time-integrated activity concentrations in domestically produced goats' milk compared with commercially produced cows' milk range between factors of 1.5 and 5 higher. This factor is dependent on both the differences in peak concentration for different radionuclides and on the relative importance of the contribution of contaminated winter feed to the intake of the cows' diet compared to the goats' diet, which comprises grass alone. For chickens' eggs, the differences in time-integrated activity concentration can range from a factor of a few to very large, depending on the radionuclide, time before the cereal harvest that deposition occurs, and the fraction of grass in the diet of domestically reared chickens. For long-lived radionuclides, the differences seen in the maximum activity concentrations are compounded because, whereas the grass consumed is subjected to natural weathering processes over the period that doses are calculated, once the cereals are harvested, they only decrease by radioactive decay over the period they are consumed by the chicken.

The detailed results are presented in the accompanying memorandum[27].

5.4 Comparison of doses

On the basis of the time-integrated activity concentrations in foods calculated as described in Section 4, estimates of committed effective doses resulting from unit deposition (1 Bq m^{-2}) have been made. The consumption rates used were assumed to be those for adults (with the exception of milk consumption, where child consumption rates were used), as discussed in Section 3. Adult ingestion dose coefficients were taken from ICRP Publication 72[28] (child dose coefficients were used for milk consumption). These normalised doses can be used to study the actual doses and the relative importance of different foods and radionuclides for any release scenario. To assist with this, Table 14 gives the deposition rates for unit release of each radionuclide, for a number of weather categories and distances from the site, as defined in the table.

The dataset of results produced from these dose calculations is very large. The detailed results are contained in the accompanying memorandum[27]. For discussion in this report, a subset of the results has been chosen to illustrate the conclusions of the study. Predictions of committed effective doses for

TABLE 14 Deposition rates following accidental release[*]

Radionuclide	Deposition rate (Bq m^{-2})					
	Weather category[†]					
	D dry		D wet		F	
	1 km	10 km	1 km	10 km	1 km	10 km
Iodine radionuclides	1.2 10^5	3.1 10^3	2.4 10^5	6.2 10^3	3.2 10^5	2.1 10^4
Other radionuclides	1.2 10^4	3.1 10^2	1.2 10^5	3.1 10^3	3.2 10^4	2.1 10^3

[*] A release of 10^{12} Bq, an effective release height of 20 m, and a release duration of 1 hour.
[†] Gaussian dispersion as recommended by a UK Working Group on Atmospheric Dispersion[29,30].

the consumption of food in the first year after deposition are presented, following deposition that occurs 30 days and 120 days before the start of harvest. Dose calculations were carried out for tritium, sulphur-35, strontium-90, iodine-131, caesium-137 and plutonium-239. However, dose calculations were not carried out for chickens' eggs contaminated with tritium or sulphur-35, nor goats' milk contaminated with tritium, owing to the scarcity of data. In the second year following deposition, the intakes of activity are lower, often by several orders of magnitude. The resulting doses are significantly lower than 1 pSv per Bq m^{-2} (this is equivalent to about 1 µSv for the release scenarios given in Table 14) and any differences between commercially and domestically produced foods are not important. These doses are only presented in the supporting memorandum[27].

5.4.1 Average consumption rates

In this section, committed effective doses based on median household *per caput* consumption rates for domestic foods (Table 6) and generalised mean consumption rates for commercially produced foods (Table 7) are discussed.

There are two factors that influence the difference in the doses per unit deposit observed. These are the time-integrated activity concentrations in the foods and the quantities of the foods consumed. The foods and radionuclides for which the activity concentrations in the foods produced under domestic practices were higher than those in commercially produced food have been discussed in Sections 5.1 and 5.3. The main conclusion of relevance here is that differences in time-integrated activity concentrations in crops tend to get larger for deposition occurring at increasing times before the start of harvest (although this is dependent on the radionuclide and the crop). For milk and eggs the situation is more complex owing to major differences in husbandry practices between commercially and domestically reared animals.

The differences in the consumption rates between domestic consumers and an average member of the population vary depending on the food, as can be seen by comparing Tables 6 and 7. For potatoes and green vegetables, the median consumption rate for domestic foods is about 80% of the corresponding generalised consumption rates; for legume vegetables, carrots and soft fruit the consumption rates are factors of about 1.5, 1.7 and 7 higher, respectively; for milk, the domestic consumption rate is about one-third lower (although the value used is uncertain).

These doses are presented in Table 15. In order to assist the comparison, where the difference between the doses from commercially and domestically produced food given in Table 15 is greater than a factor of two, the higher dose of the pair is underlined.

It can be seen that the doses are, for most foods, either very similar or higher for consumption of commercial crops. The main exceptions are those for soft fruit and for eggs, particularly when deposition occurs well before the harvest of the food crop. For soft fruit, and assuming deposition occurs 30 days before the start of harvest, the doses for domestic consumption are between a factor of five and a factor of ten higher than those for commercial consumption. This is mainly due to the difference of a factor of seven in the consumption rates between these consumers. At 120 days before the start of harvest, however, the differences range from between a factor of about seven for strontium and about a factor of one-hundred for the other radionuclides, reflecting the assumptions made about the time of crop planting. For chickens' eggs, the differences in the relative differences between the estimated doses reflect solely those in the time-integrated activity concentrations, since the same consumption rates have been assumed. In general, chickens consuming grass will produce eggs with higher activity concentrations than those consuming cereals. The relatively higher dose from caesium-137 deposited one month before harvest reflects the preferential translocation of caesium to the cereal grain and its relatively long half-life in the harvested crop.

TABLE 15 Committed effective doses per unit deposit for consumers of foods at mean consumption rates[*]

Food	Radionuclide	Dose[†] ($Sv\ Bq^{-1}\ m^2$) for deposition occurring			
		30 days before the start of harvest		120 days before the start of harvest	
		Domestic	Commercial	Domestic	Commercial
Carrots	^{3}H	$2.1\ 10^{-13}$	$1.3\ 10^{-13}$	$2.1\ 10^{-13}$	$1.3\ 10^{-13}$
	^{35}S	$2.6\ 10^{-11}$	$1.6\ 10^{-11}$	$1.4\ 10^{-12}$	$\underline{1.6\ 10^{-11}}$
	^{90}Sr	$\underline{7.8\ 10^{-11}}$	$2.5\ 10^{-11}$	$\underline{5.7\ 10^{-11}}$	$2.5\ 10^{-11}$
	^{131}I	$7.0\ 10^{-11}$	$4.7\ 10^{-11}$	$1.5\ 10^{-17}$	$\underline{4.7\ 10^{-11}}$
	^{137}Cs	$4.0\ 10^{-10}$	$3.4\ 10^{-10}$	$1.5\ 10^{-12}$	$\underline{3.4\ 10^{-10}}$
	^{239}Pu	$3.5\ 10^{-13}$	$1.9\ 10^{-13}$	$2.6\ 10^{-13}$	$1.9\ 10^{-13}$
Potatoes	^{3}H	$6.7\ 10^{-13}$	$8.9\ 10^{-13}$	$6.7\ 10^{-13}$	$8.9\ 10^{-13}$
	^{35}S	$4.6\ 10^{-11}$	$6.6\ 10^{-11}$	$3.3\ 10^{-12}$	$\underline{7.7\ 10^{-12}}$
	^{90}Sr	$4.5\ 10^{-11}$	$\underline{1.7\ 10^{-10}}$	$4.0\ 10^{-11}$	$\underline{1.5\ 10^{-10}}$
	^{31}I	$3.7\ 10^{-11}$	$\underline{1.6\ 10^{-10}}$	$4.0\ 10^{-17}$	$\underline{3.1\ 10^{-12}}$
	^{137}Cs	$1.0\ 10^{-9}$	$1.8\ 10^{-9}$	$3.1\ 10^{-12}$	$\underline{8.2\ 10^{-11}}$
	^{239}Pu	$3.6\ 10^{-13}$	$\underline{1.4\ 10^{-12}}$	$3.6\ 10^{-13}$	$\underline{1.3\ 10^{-12}}$
Green vegetables	^{3}H	$2.1\ 10^{-13}$	$2.7\ 10^{-13}$	–	–
	^{35}S	$1.2\ 10^{-10}$	$1.6\ 10^{-10}$	–	–
	^{90}Sr	$5.2\ 10^{-9}$	$6.6\ 10^{-9}$	–	–
	^{131}I	$1.5\ 10^{-9}$	$1.9\ 10^{-9}$	–	–
	^{137}Cs	$2.3\ 10^{-9}$	$3.0\ 10^{-9}$	–	–
	^{239}Pu	$4.4\ 10^{-8}$	$5.6\ 10^{-8}$	–	–
Legume vegetables	^{3}H	$3.9\ 10^{-14}$	$2.7\ 10^{-14}$	$3.9\ 10^{-14}$	$2.7\ 10^{-14}$
	^{35}S	$1.2\ 10^{-11}$	$8.0\ 10^{-12}$	$2.2\ 10^{-13}$	$2.3\ 10^{-13}$
	^{90}Sr	$5.7\ 10^{-11}$	$3.6\ 10^{-11}$	$1.3\ 10^{-11}$	$6.4\ 10^{-12}$
	^{131}I	$1.1\ 10^{-11}$	$7.2\ 10^{-12}$	$1.5\ 10^{-18}$	$\underline{3.3\ 10^{-17}}$
	^{137}Cs	$3.0\ 10^{-10}$	$2.0\ 10^{-10}$	$4.3\ 10^{-13}$	$\underline{5.5\ 10^{-12}}$
	^{239}Pu	$2.0\ 10^{-10}$	$1.3\ 10^{-10}$	$1.8\ 10^{-13}$	$\underline{1.5\ 10^{-12}}$
Soft fruit	^{3}H	$\underline{1.4\ 10^{-13}}$	$2.1\ 10^{-14}$	$\underline{1.4\ 10^{-13}}$	$2.1\ 10^{-14}$
	^{35}S	$\underline{4.2\ 10^{-11}}$	$6.6\ 10^{-12}$	$\underline{1.3\ 10^{-12}}$	$1.2\ 10^{-13}$
	^{90}Sr	$\underline{1.6\ 10^{-10}}$	$2.5\ 10^{-11}$	$\underline{8.3\ 10^{-12}}$	$1.3\ 10^{-12}$
	^{131}I	$\underline{3.8\ 10^{-11}}$	$5.8\ 10^{-12}$	$\underline{1.7\ 10^{-16}}$	$1.8\ 10^{-18}$
	^{137}Cs	$\underline{1.1\ 10^{-9}}$	$1.6\ 10^{-10}$	$\underline{2.9\ 10^{-11}}$	$1.3\ 10^{-13}$
	^{239}Pu	$\underline{6.9\ 10^{-10}}$	$1.1\ 10^{-10}$	$\underline{8.1\ 10^{-12}}$	$8.4\ 10^{-14}$
Eggs	^{90}Sr	$\underline{2.8\ 10^{-10}}$	$1.3\ 10^{-10}$	$\underline{2.8\ 10^{-10}}$	$2.6\ 10^{-12}$
	^{131}I	$\underline{5.6\ 10^{-10}}$	$1.3\ 10^{-10}$	$\underline{5.6\ 10^{-10}}$	$2.5\ 10^{-16}$
	^{137}Cs	$1.6\ 10^{-10}$	$\underline{5.5\ 10^{-10}}$	$1.6\ 10^{-10}$	$2.1\ 10^{-11}$
	^{239}Pu	$\underline{4.8\ 10^{-11}}$	$1.1\ 10^{-11}$	$\underline{4.8\ 10^{-11}}$	$2.2\ 10^{-13}$
Goats' milk[‡]	^{35}S	$\underline{1.8\ 10^{-8}}$	$6.0\ 10^{-9}$	–	–
	^{90}Sr	$1.9\ 10^{-8}$	$1.5\ 10^{-8}$	–	–
	^{131}I	$\underline{3.6\ 10^{-8}}$	$1.1\ 10^{-8}$	–	–
	^{137}Cs	$1.1\ 10^{-8}$	$1.2\ 10^{-8}$	–	–
	^{239}Pu	$2.7\ 10^{-11}$	$2.5\ 10^{-11}$	–	–

[*] Median household *per caput* consumption rates for domestically produced foods and generalised mean consumption rates for commercially produced foods.

[†] Doses are calculated for adults from the first year's intake following deposition.

[‡] Doses from the consumption of domestically produced goats milk are compared with doses from the consumption of commercially produced cows' milk and are for 10 year old children, not adults. Doses for goats' milk are appropriate for all times of the year; doses for cows' milk are representative for an accident occurring during the grazing season.

For the other food categories, where the doses differ by more than a factor of two, it is almost always the doses from commercial products that are higher. This largely reflects the higher time-integrated activity concentrations predicted for these foods. The exception is strontium-90 in carrots. In this case, as discussed in Section 5.3, the time-integrated activity concentrations in the domestic crop are higher and this difference is reflected in the doses.

It is noticeable that the differences in doses between goats' and cows' milk are somewhat less than those in the activity concentrations. This is because the *per caput* consumption rate for goats' milk, used in this study, is somewhat lower than the corresponding mean for cows' milk. However, the uncertainty associated with the value used should be recognised (see Section 3).

5.4.2   'Critical group' consumption rates

The data presented in Table 16 show the predicted doses for the consumption of food at the 97.5th percentile of the consumption rate distributions for consumers of both domestic and commercial foods. In order to assist the comparison, where the difference between the doses from commercially and domestically produced food given in Table 16 is greater than a factor of two, the higher dose of the pair is underlined.

The differences between the doses for domestic consumers and consumers in the general population do not necessarily show the same trends as seen in Table 15 for average consumption. This results from relative differences in the ratio of consumption rates between domestic and general consumers for average and 97.5th percentile groups. For legume vegetables and soft fruit the 97.5th percentiles of the domestic food consumption rate distributions are factors of 23 and 14 higher than those for consumers of commercial foods, respectively; these can be compared with the factors of 1.5 and 7 observed for the average consumption rates. For the doses from legume vegetables for deposition occurring 30 days before the start of harvest this larger difference in consumption rate increases the difference in doses observed, the doses for domestic consumers now being about a factor of 20 higher. For deposition occurring 120 days before the start of harvest, the relatively higher domestic consumption rates lead to the doses from caesium-137 and plutonium-239 for domestic and general consumers being very similar, whilst doses to domestic consumers from strontium-90 are about a factor of 30 higher. Similarly, for fruit, the doses from domestic consumption are relatively higher reflecting the higher consumption rates. The relatively higher consumption rates of domestically produced potatoes compared to those produced commercially results in the doses from domestically produced potatoes being more similar for both times before the start of harvest, in contrast to that seen for average consumers.

6   Implications for nuclear accident response

In emergency exercises, MAFF has based its advice to domestic consumers on the commercial situation. Were MAFF formally to adopt such an approach, advice to the domestic consumer would only need to be modified with respect to advice appropriate for commercially produced foods, where the conditions of domestic production might lead to higher maximum activity concentrations or doses. Overall, this study has shown that it is unlikely that maximum activity concentrations in domestic foods or doses received from the consumption of such foods would be factors of more than two or three higher than those estimated for commercial foods. For most situations they would be expected to be comparable or lower. However, this study has highlighted a few areas where additional caution might be appropriate. It has also eliminated several factors that may have been thought in the past to enhance doses to the domestic consumer.

TABLE 16 Committed effective doses per unit deposit for consumers of foods at critical group consumption rates*

Food	Radionuclide	Dose[†] (Sv Bq^{-1} m^2) for deposition occurring			
		30 days before the start of harvest		120 days before the start of harvest	
		Domestic	Commercial	Domestic	Commercial
Carrots	^{3}H	$1.0\ 10^{-12}$	$5.0\ 10^{-13}$	$1.0\ 10^{-12}$	$5.0\ 10^{-13}$
	^{35}S	$1.3\ 10^{-10}$	$6.5\ 10^{-11}$	$7.1\ 10^{-12}$	$\underline{6.5\ 10^{-11}}$
	^{90}Sr	$\underline{3.8\ 10^{-10}}$	$1.0\ 10^{-10}$	$2.8\ 10^{-10}$	$1.0\ 10^{-10}$
	^{131}I	$3.4\ 10^{-10}$	$1.9\ 10^{-10}$	$7.5\ 10^{-17}$	$\underline{1.9\ 10^{-10}}$
	^{137}Cs	$1.9\ 10^{-9}$	$1.4\ 10^{-9}$	$7.5\ 10^{-12}$	$\underline{1.4\ 10^{-9}}$
	^{239}Pu	$1.7\ 10^{-12}$	$7.6\ 10^{-13}$	$1.3\ 10^{-12}$	$7.6\ 10^{-13}$
Potatoes	^{3}H	$4.2\ 10^{-12}$	$2.1\ 10^{-12}$	$\underline{4.2\ 10^{-12}}$	$2.1\ 10^{-12}$
	^{35}S	$2.9\ 10^{-10}$	$1.6\ 10^{-10}$	$2.0\ 10^{-11}$	$1.8\ 10^{-11}$
	^{90}Sr	$2.8\ 10^{-10}$	$4.1\ 10^{-10}$	$2.5\ 10^{-10}$	$3.7\ 10^{-10}$
	^{131}I	$2.3\ 10^{-10}$	$3.8\ 10^{-10}$	$2.5\ 10^{-16}$	$\underline{7.4\ 10^{-12}}$
	^{137}Cs	$6.5\ 10^{-9}$	$4.2\ 10^{-9}$	$2.0\ 10^{-11}$	$\underline{2.0\ 10^{-10}}$
	^{239}Pu	$2.2\ 10^{-12}$	$3.3\ 10^{-12}$	$2.3\ 10^{-12}$	$3.0\ 10^{-12}$
Green vegetables	^{3}H	$1.2\ 10^{-12}$	$8.0\ 10^{-13}$	–	–
	^{35}S	$6.9\ 10^{-10}$	$4.7\ 10^{-10}$	–	–
	^{90}Sr	$2.9\ 10^{-8}$	$2.0\ 10^{-8}$	–	–
	^{131}I	$8.5\ 10^{-9}$	$5.8\ 10^{-9}$	–	–
	^{137}Cs	$1.3\ 10^{-8}$	$8.9\ 10^{-9}$	–	–
	^{239}Pu	$2.5\ 10^{-7}$	$1.7\ 10^{-7}$	–	–
Legume vegetables	^{3}H	$\underline{1.7\ 10^{-12}}$	$7.3\ 10^{-14}$	$\underline{1.7\ 10^{-12}}$	$7.3\ 10^{-14}$
	^{35}S	$\underline{5.2\ 10^{-10}}$	$2.2\ 10^{-11}$	$\underline{9.8\ 10^{-12}}$	$6.4\ 10^{-13}$
	^{90}Sr	$\underline{2.5\ 10^{-9}}$	$9.7\ 10^{-11}$	$\underline{5.5\ 10^{-10}}$	$1.8\ 10^{-11}$
	^{131}I	$\underline{4.7\ 10^{-10}}$	$2.0\ 10^{-11}$	$6.3\ 10^{-17}$	$9.0\ 10^{-17}$
	^{137}Cs	$\underline{1.3\ 10^{-8}}$	$5.4\ 10^{-10}$	$1.9\ 10^{-11}$	$1.5\ 10^{-11}$
	^{239}Pu	$\underline{8.7\ 10^{-9}}$	$3.5\ 10^{-10}$	$7.9\ 10^{-12}$	$4.2\ 10^{-12}$
Soft fruit	^{3}H	$\underline{1.2\ 10^{-12}}$	$8.0\ 10^{-14}$	$\underline{1.2\ 10^{-12}}$	$8.0\ 10^{-14}$
	^{35}S	$\underline{3.4\ 10^{-10}}$	$2.5\ 10^{-11}$	$\underline{1.0\ 10^{-11}}$	$4.4\ 10^{-13}$
	^{90}Sr	$\underline{1.3\ 10^{-9}}$	$9.5\ 10^{-11}$	$\underline{6.8\ 10^{-11}}$	$4.8\ 10^{-12}$
	^{131}I	$\underline{3.1\ 10^{-10}}$	$2.2\ 10^{-11}$	$\underline{1.4\ 10^{-15}}$	$6.9\ 10^{-18}$
	^{137}Cs	$\underline{8.6\ 10^{-9}}$	$6.2\ 10^{-10}$	$\underline{2.3\ 10^{-10}}$	$4.9\ 10^{-13}$
	^{239}Pu	$\underline{5.6\ 10^{-9}}$	$4.0\ 10^{-10}$	$\underline{6.6\ 10^{-11}}$	$3.2\ 10^{-13}$
Eggs	^{90}Sr	$\underline{8.1\ 10^{-10}}$	$3.8\ 10^{-10}$	$\underline{8.1\ 10^{-10}}$	$7.6\ 10^{-12}$
	^{131}I	$\underline{1.7\ 10^{-9}}$	$3.9\ 10^{-11}$	$\underline{1.7\ 10^{-9}}$	$7.3\ 10^{-16}$
	^{137}Cs	$\underline{4.8\ 10^{-10}}$	$1.6\ 10^{-9}$	$\underline{4.8\ 10^{-10}}$	$6.3\ 10^{-11}$
	^{239}Pu	$\underline{1.4\ 10^{-10}}$	$3.1\ 10^{-11}$	$\underline{1.4\ 10^{-10}}$	$6.4\ 10^{-13}$
Goats' milk[‡]	^{35}S	$\underline{3.2\ 10^{-8}}$	$1.3\ 10^{-8}$	–	–
	^{90}Sr	$3.4\ 10^{-8}$	$3.3\ 10^{-8}$	–	–
	^{131}I	$6.6\ 10^{-8}$	$2.3\ 10^{-8}$	–	–
	^{137}Cs	$2.0\ 10^{-8}$	$2.7\ 10^{-8}$	–	–
	^{239}Pu	$4.8\ 10^{-11}$	$5.5\ 10^{-11}$	–	–

* 97.5th percentile household *per caput* consumption rates for domestically produced foods and generalised 97.5th percentile consumption rates for commercially produced foods.
† Doses are calculated for adults from the first year's intake following deposition.
‡ Doses from the consumption of domestically produced goats' milk are compared with doses from the consumption of commercially produced cows' milk and are for 10 year old children, not adults. Doses for goats' milk are appropriate for all times of the year; doses for cows' milk are representative for an accident occurring during the grazing season.

6.1 Activity concentrations

In general, there are no significant differences in the predicted maximum activity concentrations in domestically and commercially produced foods, reflecting the similar agricultural practices that are adopted. The study has identified, however, several cases where the maximum activity concentrations in domestically produced foods may be significantly higher than in those produced commercially.

When deposition occurs a long time before the start of harvest, the maximum activity concentrations predicted are very sensitive to whether or not it is assumed that a particular crop has already been planted. In this study, it has been assumed that commercial soft fruit production is dominated by strawberries, whereas domestic production is dominated by fruit grown on bushes. These assumptions have resulted in estimated maximum activity concentrations in domestic crops that are typically a factor of about 100 higher than those in commercially produced fruit, for deposition occurring 120 days before harvest. This sensitivity to planting times needs to be addressed by MAFF when developing specific advice after an accident.

For chickens' eggs, if it is assumed that domestic chickens are fed only on grass, then the maximum activity concentrations are significantly higher for domestically reared chickens compared with those reared commercially for all the radionuclides considered. However, in reality, domestic chickens are likely to be fed on a mixed diet of grass and cereals, in which case the maximum activity concentrations would become more similar for most radionuclides for times where deposition occurs close to the cereal harvest. For deposition occurring at long times before the start of harvest, the maximum activity concentrations in domestically produced eggs would always be more restrictive. The implication of these data for MAFF advice is that the activity concentrations in eggs produced from domestically reared chickens are likely to be higher than those in commercial eggs and a reduction in any grass component of the diet may be pertinent. In order to refine this advice, more specific information on husbandry practices for domestically reared chickens is required. It should also be noted that data on the transfer of radionuclides to eggs are very sparse and the data presented should only be used to indicate the differences in activity concentrations that might be observed and not used as absolute values.

The maximum activity concentrations in goats' milk are likely to be about a factor of three to five times higher than those for cows' milk whilst the animals are grazing grass. Using this information, advice to domestic producers of goats' milk can be based on measurements made in cows' milk as long as both animals are grazing pasture at the time of deposition. If an accident occurs while cows are indoors being fed stored feed whilst domestically reared goats were still grazing outdoors, this approach cannot be used, and it would be necessary either to estimate or to measure the actual activity concentrations in the goats' milk.

The maximum activity concentrations of tritium in domestically and commercially produced crops are assumed to be the same, reflecting the scope of the model. However, the maximum concentration in vegetables produced in gardens could be higher than those seen in the commercially produced crop if the vegetables are harvested and eaten within a few hours of the occurrence of deposition. This is due to the initial intake of tritiated water by the plant leaves.

Differences in the delays between harvest and consumption of domestically and commercially produced crops may also lead to differences between the activity concentrations at the time of consumption for short-lived radionuclides, such as iodine-131. Commercially produced vegetables and fruit grown for fresh consumption are largely marketed through retail outlets. This leads to a delay of typically a few days. Domestic growers, however, tend to grow and harvest crops on a seasonal basis for immediate consumption and so guarantee a fresh supply of vegetables and fruit over as much of the year as possible. The delay between harvest and consumption is therefore, in general, likely to be shorter than that from commercially produced vegetables and fruit leading to higher activity concentrations at the time of consumption. This is also the case for tritium because, after harvest, the vegetables start to dry out quite quickly and tritium is therefore lost. This could lead to noticeable differences in the maximum activity concentrations in the vegetables at the time of consumption although information is not available to quantify this.

Other factors have been raised as potentially giving rise to increased activity concentrations in domestically cultivated crops. These include differences in the species of vegetables grown, fertilising and composting methods and the use of collected water for irrigation. It is unlikely that these would give rise to any significant differences between domestically cultivated crops and those produced commercially. One possible exception may be where a domestic producer uses water collected during deposition for irrigating plants shortly after an accident has occurred. In such circumstances, it may be prudent for MAFF to suggest that the contents of water butts should not be used to irrigate domestic crops after an accident has occurred.

6.2   Doses

If the foods for which time-integrated activity concentrations are higher are also consumed in relatively higher quantities by domestic consumers, this can lead to significant differences in the doses that could be expected. Also, even if activity concentrations in domestically produced food are similar or slightly lower than those predicted in commercially produced foods, high consumption rates by domestic consumers may give rise to the doses for domestic consumers being higher, particularly for critical group consumers.

In general, the average doses predicted for domestic consumers are either lower or within a factor of two of those predicted for the consumption of commercially produced foods. Notable exceptions are soft fruit and eggs, where large differences may be seen in the time-integrated activity concentrations, particularly for deposition at long times before the start of harvest. For soft fruit these are compounded by high consumption by domestic consumers compared with generalised consumption rates.

The difference in consumption rates between domestic consumers and individuals consuming commercially produced foods becomes more important when critical groups are considered. In particular, at the 97.5th percentile of the distributions, domestic consumption rates derived in this study for legume vegetables and soft fruit are more than ten times higher than those for the general population. This is reflected directly in large differences in the resulting doses. However, for other crops the differences in doses are much smaller. Although 'critical group' doses have been estimated for the consumption of goats' milk and eggs, the uncertainty surrounding the consumption rates used makes it difficult to draw firm conclusions for these foods. It seems likely, however, that due to the consumption of milk from domestically reared goats being restricted by their productivity, the dose received by an extreme consumer of goats' milk would be similar to that for an extreme consumer of cows' milk.

6.3   Regional practices

There are regional variations in the crop species grown commercially throughout England and Wales. In contrast, all of the foods considered are cultivated domestically across both countries, the variations in climatic temperature being compensated for by the cultivation of different varieties of a crop or different sowing and harvesting dates. This may also affect the adequacy of the MAFF advice to domestic consumers if based solely on the commercial situation because if a particular crop is not grown commercially in part of the country, this does not mean that an individual is not cultivating that crop domestically in his/her allotment or kitchen garden.

7   Conclusions

This study shows that, in general, the current MAFF emergency procedures for protecting domestic consumers are adequate. More specifically, by basing advice to domestic producers and consumers on the commercial situation, activity concentrations in domestically cultivated crops and doses to the average domestic consumer will not be significantly underestimated compared to those from food of a commercial origin. It would, however, be prudent to give explicit consideration to high rate consumers of domestic legume vegetables and soft fruit. It also seems likely that activity concentrations in domestically produced chickens' eggs and goats' milk will be higher than in the commercial products, although the estimates produced in this study are subject to considerable uncertainty, and, for goats' milk, the difference will probably only be about a factor of three to five. Other factors that MAFF should consider are:

(a)   differences in agricultural practices, such as variations in growing periods between commercial and domestic crops,

(b)   irrigation of domestic crops using water butts,

(c)   potential geographical variations in crop types grown.

This study has also highlighted some areas where data are required in order to address more realistically activity concentrations and doses arising from the domestic production of food. In particular, data on husbandry practices for goats and chickens and the transfer of radionuclides to goats' milk and chickens' eggs are sparse and consumption rates of these foods by domestic consumers are not readily available.

In considering the findings in this report it should be remembered that domestic consumers represent only a small proportion of the UK population: in the National Food Survey undertaken by MAFF in 1993, fewer than 100 out of 8000 households consumed any domestically grown produce.

8   Acknowledgements

This study was funded by MAFF under contract number SA075. Thanks are expressed to Ms Melanie Wright, of the Data Archive Unit, University of Essex, for supplying the MAFF food survey database and to Mr Geoff Stokes, of the National Society of Allotment and Leisure Gardeners, for useful information and discussion.

9   References

1   EC. Council Regulation (EURATOM) No. 3954/87 laying down the maximum permitted levels of radioactive contamination of foodstuffs and feedingstuffs following a nuclear accident or any other case of radiological emergency. *Off. J. Eur. Commun.*, L371/11 (1987), amended by Council Regulation 2218/89. *Off. J. Eur. Commun.*, L211/1 (1989).

2   EC. Council Regulation (EURATOM) No. 944/89 laying down the maximum permitted levels of radioactive contamination in minor foodstuffs following a nuclear accident or any other case of radiological emergency. *Off. J. Eur. Commun.*, L101/17 (1989).

3   Thorpe, H. The homely allotment. *Geography*, **56**, 169–83 (1975).

4   Mintel Leisure Intelligence. Produce Gardening. *Mintel Leisure Intelligence*, **3**, 1–23 (1987).

5   Saunders, P. Towards allotments 2000: national survey of allotment gardeners views in England and Wales 1993. National Society of Allotment and Leisure Gardeners Ltd (1993).

6   The garden superintendent. The vegetable plot 1975. *The Northern Gardener*, **3(1)**, 21–3 (1975).

7   Brown, J, and Simmonds, J R. FARMLAND: a dynamic model for the transfer of radionuclides through terrestrial foodchains. Chilton, NRPB-R273 (1995).

8   MacCarthy, D. Prodfact 1988. A comprehensive guide to British agricultural and horticultural produce. London, British Food Information Service (1988).

9   Potato Marketing Board. Potatoes. Economic geography, A study pack. Wakefield, B T A Limited (1982).

10   Hessayon, D G. *The Fruit Expert*. Waltham Cross, pbi publications (1990).

11   Hessayon, D G. *The Vegetable Expert*. Waltham Cross, pbi publications (1985).

12   *The Outsiders Guide to Horticulture 1995*. Lincoln, Outsiders Guide (1995).

13   Thear, K. *Part-time Farming*. London, Ward Lock (1982).

14   MAFF. National Food Survey 1993: annual report on household food consumption and expenditure. London, HMSO (1994).

15   Mondon, K. MAFF, London. Personal communication (1997).

16   Robinson, C A. Generalised habit data for radiological assessments. Chilton, NRPB-M636 (1996).

17   Higgins, N A, Shaw, P V, Haywood, S M, and Jones, J A. TRIF: a dynamic model for predicting the transfer of tritium through the terrestrial foodchain. Chilton, NRPB-R278 (1996).

18   Mayes, R W, Eayres, H F, Lamb, C S, Beresford, N A, Barnett, C L, and Howard, B J. Studies on the transfer of sulphur-35 to goat milk. Grange-over-Sands, Institute of Terrestrial Ecology (1992).

19   Coughtrey, P J. Radioactivity transfer to animal products. Luxembourg, EC, EUR 12608 (1990).

20   Hoffman, F O. A review of measured values of the milk transfer coefficient for iodine. *Health Phys.*, **35(2)**, 413–15 (1978).

21   Johnson, J E, Ward, G M, Ennis, M E, Jr, and Boamah, K N. Transfer coefficients of selected radionuclides to animal products 1. Comparison of milk and meat from dairy cows and goats. *Health Phys.,* **54(2),** 161–6 (1988).

22   Lengemann, F W. Radioiodine in the milk of cows and goats after oral administration of radioiodate and radioiodine. *Health Phys.*, **17**, 565–9 (1969).

23   MAFF/WO. Radionuclide levels in food, animals and agricultural products – post-Chernobyl monitoring in England and Wales. London, HMSO (1987).

24   Simmonds, J R, Lawson, G, and Mayall, A. Methodology for assessing the radiological consequences of routine releases of radionuclides to the environment. Luxembourg, EC, EUR 15760 (1995).

25   Green, N, Wilkins, B T, Hammond, D J, and Davidson, M F. Transfer of radionuclides to vegetables and other crops in an area of land reclaimed from the sea: a compilation of data. Chilton, NRPB-M538 (1995).

26   Nisbet, A F. NRPB, Chilton. Personal communication (1997).

27   Brown, J, Smith, J G, and Jones, A L. Differences between activity concentrations and doses arising from domestic and commercial food production in England and Wales: detailed results. Chilton, NRPB-M1081 (1999).

28   ICRP. Age-dependent doses to members of the public from intake of radionuclides: Part 5. Compilation of ingestion and inhalation dose coefficients. ICRP Publication 72. *Ann. ICRP*, **26(1)** (1996).

29   Clarke, R H. The first report of a Working Group on Atmospheric Dispersion. A model for short and medium range dispersion of radionuclides released to the atmosphere. Harwell, NRPB-R91 (1979).

30   Jones, J A. The second report of a Working Group on Atmospheric Dispersion: a procedure to include deposition in the model for short and medium range atmospheric dispersion of radionuclides. Chilton, NRPB-R122 (1981).

APPENDIX A

Agricultural Practices for Domestic and Commercial Production of Crops

J Brown and C A Tournette

1   Legume vegetables

The main species of legumes that have been considered as important to commercial and domestic production are runner beans, french beans, broad beans and peas. Commercially, the beans marketed for fresh consumption are mainly runner beans and broad beans, while those marketed frozen are french beans and broad beans. The majority of commercially produced peas are marketed frozen, the remainder being canned, dried or sold fresh on 'Pick-Your-Own' farms.

1.1   Commercial production

Beans are sown between February and June, and are available on the market from UK producers from the end of May to the beginning of October. Broad beans are harvested in the earlier part of the summer, french beans can be picked until early autumn, and runner beans which are sown relatively late in May, are harvested over the summer. Peas are sown between February and the beginning of June, depending on the climate and are harvested between July and September.

Runner beans and french beans are only grown commercially in the southern half of England as they require warm temperatures, whereas broad beans can be grown further north. Peas are grown all over England and Wales, with most of the fresh peas coming from the southern half of England.

1.2   Domestic production

Domestic growers typically sow broad beans from mid-February to the end of May and harvest them between mid-May and mid-October. French beans are sown from early May to mid-July and harvested between mid-June and the end of October. Runner beans are sown from mid-May to mid-June and harvested between mid-July and the end of October. Peas are sown between mid-March and mid-July and are harvested as they are ready, which is typically from mid-May to mid-October, although the harvesting season is likely to be shorter in the north.

In the north of England, sowing and harvesting periods for domestically grown legumes are typically shorter and within those seen commercially. In the south of England, the milder climate allows gardeners to grow legumes over longer periods, and harvesting could occur outside the standard commercial dates.

2   Root vegetables

The main species of root vegetables that have been considered as important to commercial and domestic production are potatoes, leeks, onions, carrots, parsnips, swede, turnips and beetroot. Potatoes and carrots are marketed fresh and processed, parsnips, turnips and swede are typically marketed fresh and the majority of the beetroot produced is marketed in a processed form.

2.1   Commercial production

Commercially, two potato crops are grown in a year, an early crop (commonly called new potatoes) and a main crop. Early potatoes are immature and do not keep, whereas the main crop potatoes can be kept in stores, or left in the ground to be marketed over the following nine months. The early crop is planted in February and March and is harvested between April and July. They are followed by the 'second earlies', which bridge the gap in the harvest between the earlies and the main crop. Main crop potatoes are planted in late March and April, for lifting in September and October.

Leeks can be harvested virtually all year round and are available from UK growers from July to April. The leek plants are sown directly or transplanted into the fields during March and April, and are mainly harvested from September to April. Commercially grown onions can supply the UK market all year-round. The main crop, which is planted in the spring and lifted from late August, can be stored until the next May and winter-hardy varieties of onion planted in August provide mature bulbs in June and July.

Commercial growers aim to harvest root vegetables throughout as much of the year as possible. Carrots are grown all year round from a succession of drillings of different varieties. Carrots are supplied through the winter from crops covered with soil to protect them from frost; in late winter up to May, they are covered with black polythene and straw. Parsnips are sown from February to early May. Successive drillings of different varieties ensure the continuity of the supply throughout most of the year (August to April), although the demand is stronger during the winter. Swedes are produced commercially to supply the market all year round. Sowings are made between March and July and an extended harvesting period from September to May is now possible by raising seedlings under glass before transplanting to the field. Most turnip crops are raised from successive sowing outdoors leading to a harvesting period of mid-October to mid-March. Some early varieties of turnips are grown under plastic covers to achieve a summer harvest between April and July. Commercially, beetroot is sown from March to July. The early new-season's beetroots are harvested at the end of June. The main crop is harvested mechanically from July until November for storage in clamps or barns with ventilation, or in cold stores, and marketed through the following year until early June. Much of the crop is grown for processing.

The production of the different root vegetables is spread across England and parts of Wales. Early potatoes are only grown in Cornwall, Pembrokeshire, Kent and Jersey. Main crop potatoes are grown across most of England and Wales, with production largely concentrated along the east coast. Most commercially produced dry bulb onions are grown in East Anglia, Lincolnshire and the south-east, as they require warm and sunny conditions. Carrots are mainly grown in East Anglia, Lancashire and Cheshire, Scotland and East Midlands. Parsnips are grown in most areas, but significant production comes from East Anglia and the West Midlands. Most of the swedes grown in England and Wales for culinary purposes are produced in Devon. (Scotland is the main producer of swedes.) Early varieties of turnips are grown in the Home Counties, Cheshire and Lancashire; the important areas for the main crop are Lincolnshire, Devon, Norfolk, Lancashire and Dyfed. Beetroot is mainly cultivated in Humberside and South Yorkshire, Cambridgeshire and Lancashire (including Merseyside and Greater Manchester).

2.2   Domestic production

Domestic growers usually only cultivate the early potato crop, although this is not as early as the commercial early crop. The potatoes are typically planted between mid-March and mid-May depending on the climate and lifted between mid-June and mid-October. Main crop varieties are not usually grown as they are cheap to buy, readily available from shops and require substantial space to grow. Some gardeners, however, may still have potatoes in the ground almost all year round.

Leeks are usually sown between early March and the end of April, although sowing can be extended until mid-June. The plants are transplanted in June and July and lifted between September and the middle of May. As for commercial practices, leeks are available for consumption all year round. Onion sets are planted between mid-February and the end of April and are lifted between July and September depending on the climate for storage. Japanese winter-hardy varieties are now also available to domestic growers to enable them to produce an earlier crop in June and July.

Domestic growers could grow carrots all year round, but it is more usual to sow outdoors between mid-March and mid-July, and possibly again in August and to lift the crop from June until the end of December. The crop is left in the ground and eaten as required. February is the traditional month for sowing parsnips in gardens and allotments, although in the north of the country it may be in March or April, once the ground is warmer. Parsnips keep well in the ground and the crop is lifted from mid-October to mid-March, as required. Domestically, swedes are sown by gardeners between mid-April and mid-June, to be lifted throughout the autumn and the winter, from mid-September to the end of March. As for carrots, turnips could also be grown by gardeners all year round, but the main sowing seasons are March to June and mid-July to the end of September, producing crops for harvest between mid-October and mid-March, and mid-May to the end of September, respectively. Typical dates for sowing beetroot outdoors are mid-March to the end of July. These are harvested between mid-May and mid-November in central and southern England and Wales and over a much shorter period in the north of England.

3 Green vegetables

The main species of green vegetables that have been considered as important to commercial and domestic production are broccoli (calabrese), brussels sprouts, cabbages (summer, winter and spring varieties), cauliflowers (several varieties too) and lettuces.

3.1 Commercial production

Cabbages and lettuces are harvested throughout the year from a succession of sowings. Broccoli is typically planted between February and August and harvested between May and November. Cauliflowers are usually planted between March and May and are harvested between May and December, depending on the variety. Brussels sprouts are grown for harvest between August and March.

Cabbages, brussels sprouts and lettuces are grown in most counties of England and Wales. The majority of the cauliflower production comes from south Lincolnshire except for winter-heading types which are mostly grown in West Cornwall and Jersey.

3.2 Domestic production

Similarly to commercial practices, cabbage and lettuce are harvested throughout the year from a succession of sowings. Domestic growers sow broccoli between early April and the end of May, plant out between early June and the end of July (later in the north of England), and harvest between mid-July and mid-November. By growing different varieties, it is possible to have an additional harvesting period from mid-January to the middle of May. Brussels sprouts are typically sown between mid-March and mid-April, planted out from early May to the end of June, and harvested between mid-September and the end of March. Cauliflowers are normally sown between mid-March and the end of May, planted out from early June, and harvested between early March and the end of November.

4 Soft fruit

The main species of soft fruit that have been considered as important to commercial and domestic production are strawberries, raspberries, gooseberries and blackcurrants. Soft fruits are very popular as 'Pick-Your-Own' crops, with strawberries being the most popular. Most of the English raspberry crop is sold fresh; however, some freezing takes place, mainly in Norfolk.

4.1   Commercial production

The outdoor growing season for strawberries in England and Wales is from late May to October; early varieties are harvested between May and July (about 70% of the total strawberry production) and 'everbearer' varieties are harvested from August to October providing an extended season. Polythene is widely used by commercial growers to advance cropping. Autumn 'everbearer' fruit varieties are usually pot-grown under protection and planted out in April, to crop from August to October. Several varieties of raspberry plants are grown commercially to ensure production between May and October, although the majority of the crop is harvested in July. Gooseberries are harvested commercially between June and August, and blackcurrants are harvested in July and August.

Strawberries are mainly produced in Kent. The main areas for growing raspberries are Kent, Hereford and Worcester and Norfolk. They are also grown to a lesser extent in Wales. Gooseberry bushes are commercially grown in many counties of England and Wales. Blackcurrants are mainly grown commercially in the West Midlands, Norfolk and Kent.

4.2   Domestic production

Most domestic growers buy young strawberry plants in late summer or early autumn to plant outside and these are left to overwinter in the ground. However, spring planting in March and April is also possible. By growing several varieties, strawberries may be picked from late May to October without the need for protecting the crop. However, the crop is typically ready for harvest in June and July. Raspberries are harvested over a two to four week period between July and October, depending on the variety. They are often frozen and preserved. Depending on the varieties grown, gardeners may pick gooseberries between the end of June and early August, although all the fruits from one bush have to be picked over one to two weeks. Blackcurrants appear to be less popular with domestic growers than other soft fruit, which may be because they are not often eaten fresh. Most varieties of blackcurrant crop in July (possibly August in the more northern regions of England) and are picked over one to two weeks.

Strawberries for domestic production are mainly grown in the southern half of England. As raspberries are late flowering plants, they are seldom affected by frost and they are grown across the whole of England and Wales. Gooseberries are easily grown and are popular with domestic growers all over England and Wales.

5   Bibliography

Potato Marketing Board. Potato storage, technical survey on potato storage practices in Great Britain. Potato Marketing Board (1994).

Hessayon, D G. *The Fruit Expert*. Waltham Cross, pbi publications (1990).

Hessayon, D G. *The Vegetable Expert*. Waltham Cross, pbi publications (1985).

The Outsiders Guide to Horticulture 1995. Lincoln, Outsiders Guide (1995).

Thear, K. *Part-time Farming*. London, Ward Lock (1982).

APPENDIX B

Distributions of Consumption Rates
for Domestic Consumers

W Meshell and S L Prosser

1   Introduction

As indicated in the main text, detailed information on consumption rates for consumers of domestic foods was obtained from the MAFF National Food Survey of over 8000 households in 1993*. However, fewer than 100 households consumed domestically produced foods. This appendix presents the detailed consumption rate information for these domestic consumers.

2   Methodology

For each household consuming domestically produced foods, the total amount of domestic consumption was recorded, together with the number of members of the household and their ages. No information was recorded on how the consumption was divided between the household members. In order to estimate individual consumption rates, and in the absence of data that would facilitate a more accurate approach, the total consumption for each household was divided by the number of household members, regardless of their ages. This is likely to have resulted in some underestimation of the upper and lower extremes of the consumption rate distribution. In particular, since these estimated consumption rates are compared in the main study with adult consumption, it should be recognised that the high rate consumption end of the distribution for actual adult consumption may have been underestimated.

For each household, the total consumption of 18 vegetables was recorded for one week during 1993. The week of the year selected for each household varied, with the result that information was recorded for each month of the year. Information is therefore presented in terms of the individual weekly consumption rate averaged over 1993, and the variation of average individual weekly consumption rate as a function of the month of consumption. In addition, the distribution of individual weekly consumption rates summed for all green vegetables, excluding legumes, is presented, as these summed values were used in the study.

3   Results

Figure B1 presents the distributions of individual weekly consumption rates averaged over 1993. These distributions are accompanied by selected information describing them: the minimum and maximum estimated consumption rates; the total number of individuals recorded as living in households that consumed the food; the geometric mean, median, 95th and 97.5th percentiles of the distribution.

Figure B2 presents the distributions of average individual weekly consumption as a function of month of the year. These clearly show the strongly seasonal consumption pattern for some crops.

---

*MAFF. National Food Survey 1993: annual report on household food consumption and expenditure. London, HMSO (1994).

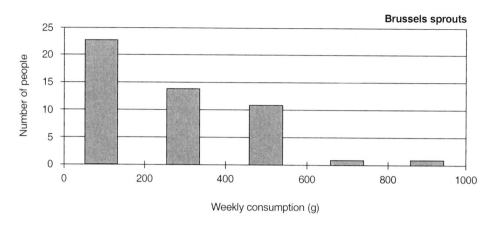

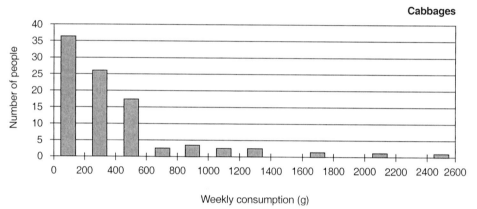

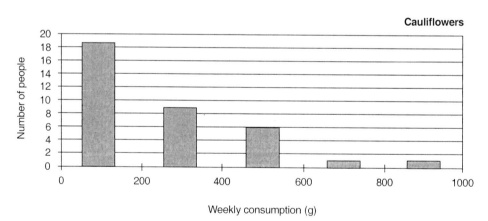

Food	Minimum (g)	Maximum (g)	Total number of people	Mean (g)	Median (g)	95th percentile (g)	97.5th percentile (g)
Brussels sprouts	38	850	50	252	227	541	669
Cabbages	34	2495	93	379	227	1225	1599
Cauliflowers	43	907	36	250	170	595	709

FIGURE B1 Distributions of individual weekly consumption rates
(a) Green vegetables

36

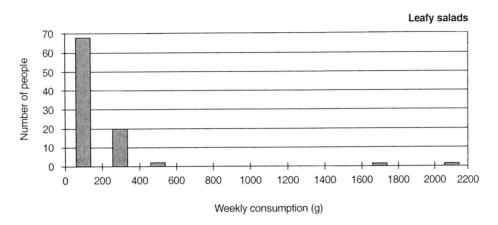

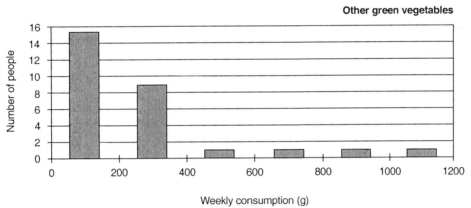

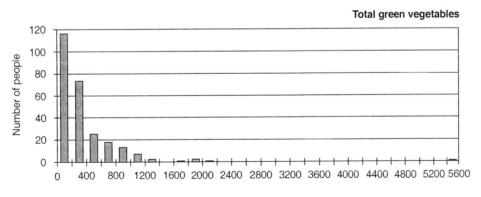

Food	Minimum (g)	Maximum (g)	Total number of people	Mean (g)	Median (g)	95th percentile (g)	97.5th percentile (g)
Leafy salads	17	2070	94	168	113	341	440
Other green vegetables	28	1021	29	229	170	842	971
Total green vegetables	17	5471	252	346	227	963	1269

FIGURE B1 Distributions of individual weekly consumption rates
(a) Green vegetables – *continued*

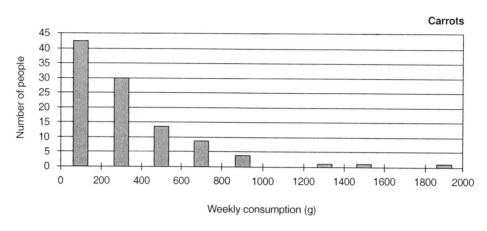

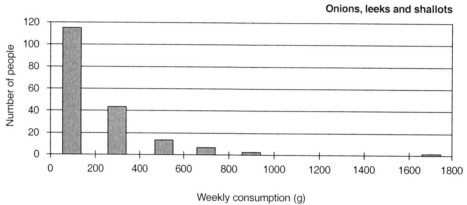

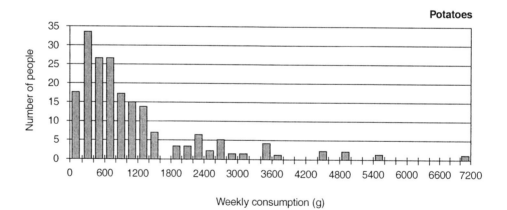

Food	Minimum (g)	Maximum (g)	Total number of people	Mean (g)	Median (g)	95th percentile (g)	97.5th percentile (g)
Carrots	13	1814	103	330	227	902	1111
Onions, leeks and shallots	7	1701	184	198	134	619	680
Potatoes	14	7031	195	1070	726	3402	4536

FIGURE B1 Distributions of individual weekly consumption rates
(b) Root vegetables

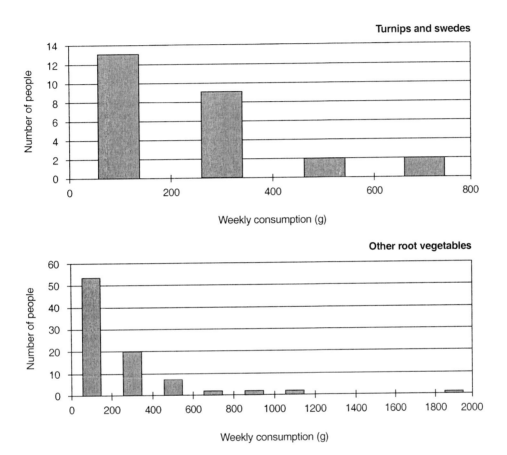

Food	Minimum (g)	Maximum (g)	Total number of people	Mean (g)	Median (g)	95th percentile (g)	97.5th percentile (g)
Turnips and swedes	23	794	26	237	211	624	723
Other root vegetables	14	1982	88	239	140	828	1001

FIGURE B1 Distributions of individual weekly consumption rates
(b) Root vegetables – *continued*

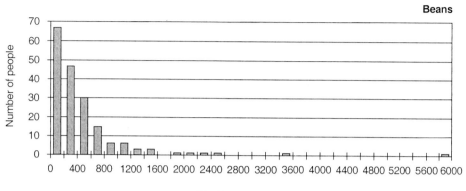

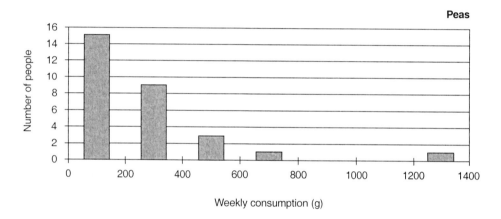

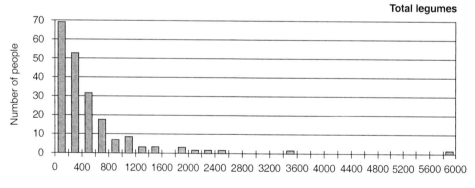

Food	Minimum (g)	Maximum (g)	Total number of people	Mean (g)	Median (g)	95th percentile (g)	97.5th percentile (g)
Beans	9	5897	180	448	255	1307	1933
Peas	28	1361	29	256	200	603	847
Total legumes	9	5897	195	452	43	1321	1848

**FIGURE B1 Distributions of individual weekly consumption rates
(c) Legumes**

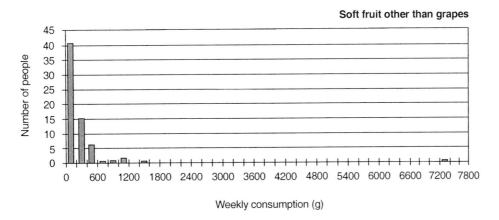

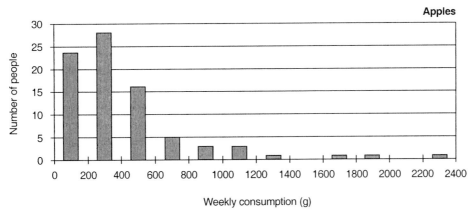

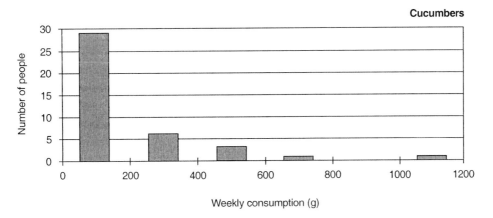

Food	Minimum (g)	Maximum (g)	Total number of people	Mean (g)	Median (g)	95th percentile (g)	97.5th percentile (g)
Soft fruits other than grapes	8	7257	68	343	151	1018	1240
Apples	19	2268	83	410	298	1134	1684
Cucumbers	28	1134	40	197	113	470	788

FIGURE B1 Distributions of individual weekly consumption rates
(d) Fruits

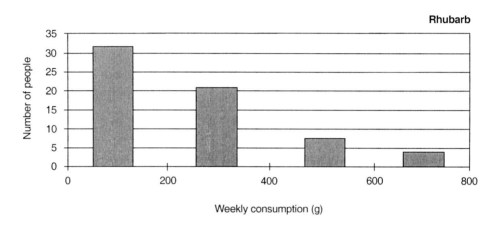

Rhubarb

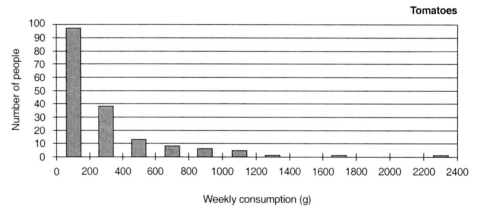

Tomatoes

Food	Minimum (g)	Maximum (g)	Total number of people	Mean (g)	Median (g)	95th percentile (g)	97.5th percentile (g)
Rhubarb	38	680	65	234	227	599	680
Tomatoes	9	2268	161	279	170	907	1134

FIGURE B1 Distributions of individual weekly consumption rates
(d) Fruits – *continued*

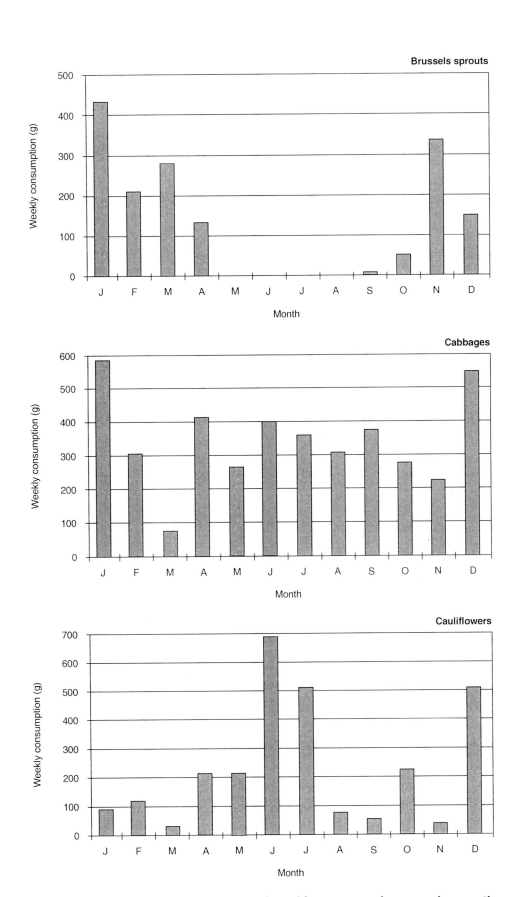

FIGURE B2 Distributions of individual weekly consumption rates by month
(a) Green vegetables

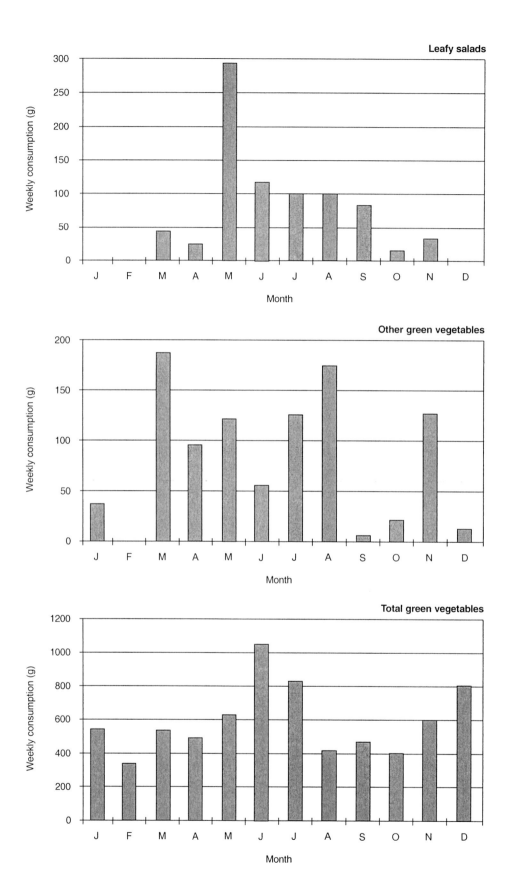

FIGURE B2 Distributions of individual weekly consumption rates by month
(a) Green vegetables – *continued*

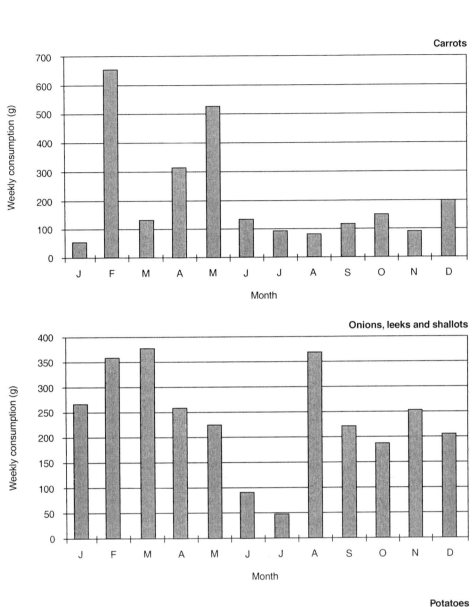

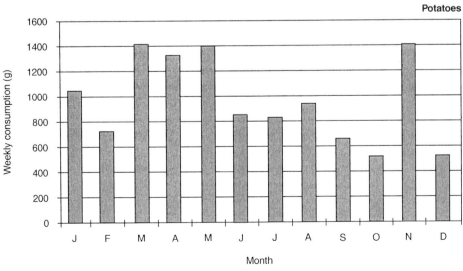

FIGURE B2 Distributions of individual weekly consumption rates by month
(b) Root vegetables

45

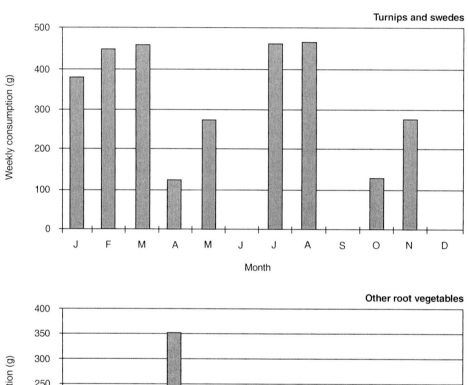

FIGURE B2 Distributions of individual weekly consumption rates by month
(b) Root vegetables – *continued*

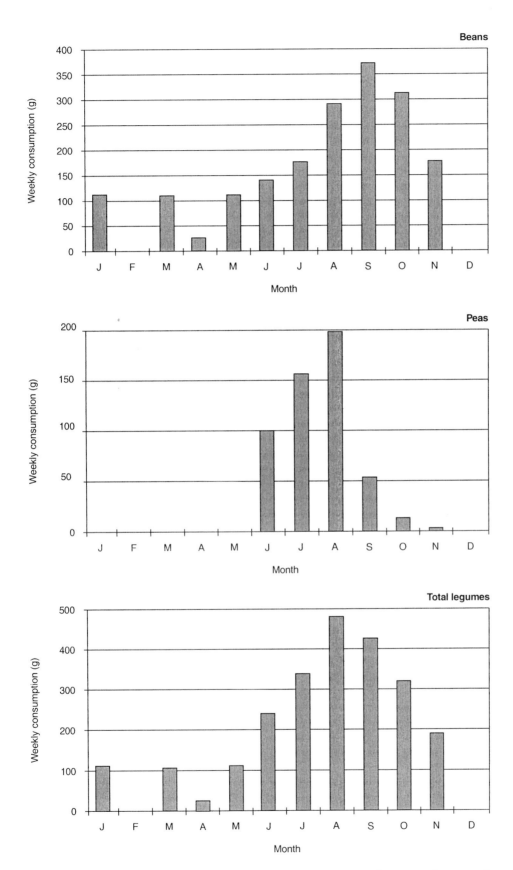

FIGURE B2 Distributions of individual weekly consumption rates by month
(c) Legumes

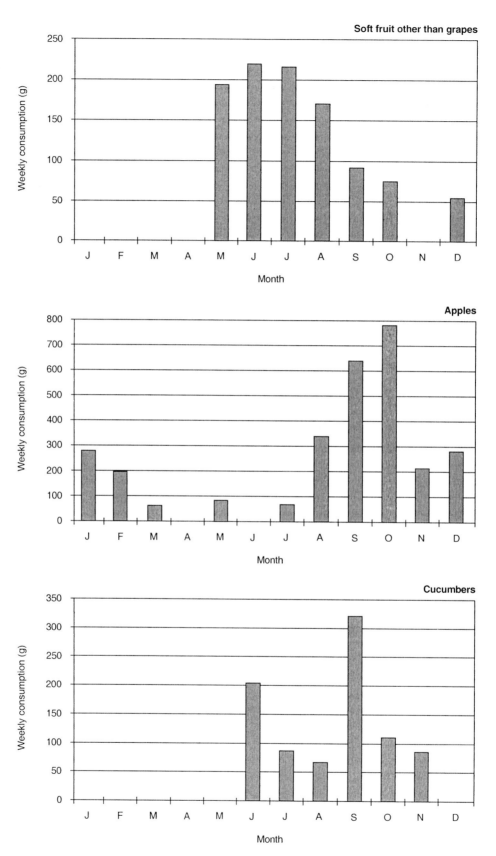

**FIGURE B2 Distributions of individual weekly consumption rates by month
(d) Fruits**

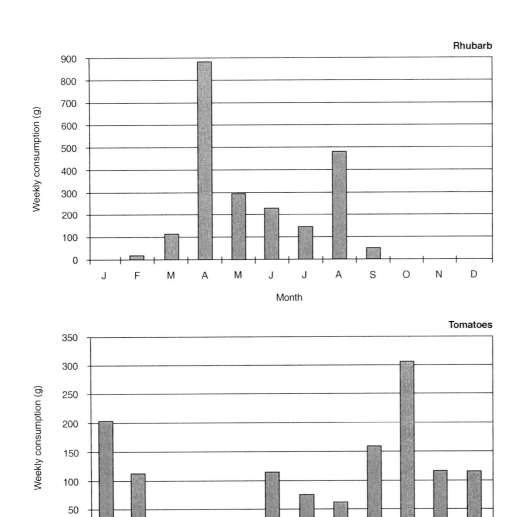

FIGURE B2 Distributions of individual weekly consumption rates by month
(d) Fruits – *continued*